Basic Queueing Theory

Brian D. Bunday,

B.Sc., Ph.D , F.S.S., F.I.M.A.

School of Mathematical Sciences, University of Bradford

Edward Arnold

© B. D. Bunday 1986

First published 1986 by
Edward Arnold (Publishers) Ltd
41 Bedford Square, London WC1B 3DQ

Edward Arnold
3 East Read Street, Baltimore,
MD21202, USA

Edward Arnold (Australia) Ltd
80 Waverley Road, Caulfield East,
Victoria 3145, Australia

British Library Cataloguing in Publication Data
Bunday, B. D.
  Basic queueing theory.
  1. Queueing theory
  I. Title
  519.8′2   T57.9

ISBN: 0-7131-3570-0

Text set in 10/12 pt Times, Atex 9000 by SB Datagraphics, Colchester
Printed and bound in Great Britain by J. W. Arrowsmith Ltd, Bristol

Preface

This book presents a course on Queueing Theory which will be suitable for a wide range of undergraduate and postgraduate courses. Students of Mathematics, Statistics and Management, along with Computing and Engineering students who are increasingly finding methods of Operational Research relevant to their needs, will find the text useful and suitable for their courses. The text arose from a set of lectures on Queueing Theory which formed part of a course on Operational Research to students of Mathematics and Statistics at the University of Bradford.

The mathematical ideas are carefully developed, although the emphasis is not on rigour. Modelling and applications lie at the heart of the book, and although some familiarity with the fundamental ideas of statistics and probability is expected, students without a strong background in this area should be able to cope with the logical and intuitive development given. Where it has been thought appropriate, numerical solutions computed with the aid of BASIC programs have been provided, along with the programs.

These BASIC programs have been written for the BBC computer but they should run with a minimum of fuss on any microcomputer. In the assignment statements LET has been omitted. On some computers it is still obligatory. The THEN has been included in IF . . . THEN GOTO statements, although on some computers either the THEN or the GOTO may be omitted. No use has been made of the IF . . . THEN . . . ELSE or the REPEAT . . . UNTIL facilities which are available on the BBC computer, but are not as yet universal. In this sense at least some of the programs are capable of refinement and the author would be delighted if students are motivated to carry out their own improvements. It is not intended that the programs are foolproof software, but it is hoped that they will serve as a vehicle to interest and motivate students. The numerical answers given are those obtained on the BBC computer. Some machines which store numbers to a different accuracy may not precisely reproduce these results although the differences will be unimportant.

Finally it is a pleasure to thank friends, colleagues and students who have in many ways contributed to this work, either through discussion over the years on queueing problems, or as guinea-pigs for many of the examples. Particularly I would mention, Dr Demetres Kouvatsos who kindly read the manuscript and suggested a number of improvements, Mr C. Mack who introduced me to the machine interference problem, and Andrew Bunday who drew the original diagrams for Fig. 6.1. Last but not least I must thank Mrs Valerie Hunter who transformed my messy manuscript into a neat and well laid out typescript.

BRIAN BUNDAY
1986

Contents

1
The Components of
a Queueing System

1.1 Introduction

We have all had experience of queues in our day to day lives. We have all had to queue for our lunch at the self service refectory, or queue at the check-out in the supermarket, or wait at the surgery in order to consult our doctor. The time lost, we may accept either philosophically as part of life's rich pattern, or with considerable annoyance, particularly if we have an important appointment later. Of course, in these situations, the delays which occur, although frustrating and causing us personal inconvenience are not necessarily expensive.

If the *customers* in the queue are aeroplanes, forced to circle an airport because the runway is not free for landing, or ships at sea, forced to wait outside the harbour because there are no free berths at which to unload their cargoes, then the delay could be very expensive indeed. The cost of the fuel consumed, the wages for the crew, insurance whilst at sea have all to be met and will increase with the length of the delay.

The queueing systems just outlined, and most other queueing systems can be thought to comprise three basic elements; the arrivals, the service mechanism and the queue discipline. Before we can study or model a queueing system we shall need to have an adequate description of these components of the system.

For the arrivals, we shall need to know whether they occur at regular intervals (every 5 minutes say), which could arise from a (strictly adhered to?) appointments system, or whether the pattern of arrivals is stochastic. This latter system will call for a detailed statistical description, including the average number of arrivals per minute, the mean inter-arrival time, and indeed the distribution of the inter-arrival time. Do the arrivals occur singly or in (random sized) groups? Is the statistical pattern of arrivals the same at all times or are there 'rush hours' and 'quiet spells'?

The service mechanism will be described by the number of servers available for service at any particular time and the time taken by each to *serve* a customer. This time may well be a random variable and so its distribution will need to be fully described.

In many queueing systems, and certainly in those to be treated in this book the queue discipline is that of first in first out (FIFO). However, variations on this occur in many practical situations. In some industrial processes in which part finished articles are stacked one on top of the other, the last article out may be the one taken for the next stage in production, simply because it is the one on top and so the most accessible. Again, some customers may have priority over others. In a hospital out-patients department, a patient with near fatal injuries will 'jump the queue' and get attention while others with relatively minor injuries may have to wait.

The variety of ways in which these components combine in real situations is almost without limit. The last two or three decades have seen hundreds of research papers written on queueing theory. These have advanced both our understanding of queueing systems and our ability to model more and more complex systems, and led to the development of a number of mathematical techniques suited to the analysis of these models.

1.2   The Reason for the Study of Queues

The study of queues is a component of many courses in Operational Research. Certainly the process by which we create mathematical models of such systems, which improve our understanding of these systems, and a study of the mathematical methods and problems generated by these models is of intrinsic interest to many people. However, there is a more pragmatic aspect. By improving our understanding of how the system works we hope to improve the system for the benefit of all involved. Needless to say this is likely to involve the 'cost effectiveness' in some way.

If we return to some of the examples cited earlier we can get some idea of what might be involved. Our study of the refectory queue might indicate that the hold up occurs at the cash desk. Possible solutions might be the provision of an additional cash desk, or even a system whereby lunch tickets are bought at some earlier time and handed in on entry to the counter. At the surgery an appointments system might lessen the amount of waiting. At the airport an improved traffic control system or an extra runway could lead to a more efficient and safe system.

We have of course to be careful as to what we mean by a better system. More rapid service will lead to less congestion and less waiting on the part of customers, but it will generally be more expensive to provide this faster service. The provision of a *better* service facility, which reduces the customer delay may also result in the facility being idle for a large proportion of the time. This may prove a disconcerting feature of the *solution* of the congestion problem.

Thus one of the main purposes of the study of queues, is to enable us, through our models, to predict what will happen if certain changes are made. The changes that can be made could be for example, in the pattern of arrivals, reducing the mean length of service time, increasing the number of servers or increasing the amount of room to accommodate waiting customers. Typical measures of congestion that we should like to be able to predict are the average number of customers waiting, the average length of time that they wait, and the proportion of time that the service facility is busy.

The word predict is vital here. To provide an extra check-out at a supermarket is to provide a person with a job. We should not be happy to find out later that the congestion problem had not been solved and that the person involved should be sacked. To build an additional runway at an airport could involve the expenditure of millions of pounds. To discover that it really was not necessary would be catastrophic financially.

Thus we shall develop models for simple queueing systems with the aim of being able to use these models to compute such quantities as the average waiting time, the proportion of time the server is busy etc. To develop these models we shall need to make certain assumptions about the systems under consideration. The reasonableness of these assumptions is clearly something we should question. Very often we have to accept that in order to construct a mathematical model of a queue which is *capable of solution* we have to make assumptions that are not strictly true. Our computed outcomes will then be approximate but provided this is borne in mind they can still be very useful and far better than mere guesses or hunches.

The vast literature on queueing theory has already been mentioned. Various authors have shown great ingenuity in developing and solving models for quite complex systems. There will only be space in this book to consider the simpler results but nonetheless it is hoped that they will serve as an introduction for a more profound study of the subject.

1.3 The Arrival Pattern

The Danish mathematician Erlang pioneered the early work on queues in the decade 1910–1920. Much of the work that followed during the period to the second world war, 1940, was concerned with the design of automatic telephone exchanges. Since that time queueing theory has found wide applications in industrial problems.

In the early work the arrival pattern was generally assumed to be one of completely random arrivals. Not only is this the easiest pattern to handle mathematically, but it is, as we shall see from its properties, particularly appropriate for the arrival of telephone calls at an exchange. It is not to be interpreted as some loosely irregular form of arrival pattern, but strictly as defined in what follows.

We let λ be the constant that represents the average rate of arrivals. Then for completely random arrivals, often shortened to random arrivals, if we consider any short time interval $(t, t + \delta t)$, then the probability that no customer arrives in this interval is $1 - \lambda \delta t + \circ(\delta t)$; the probability that exactly one customer arrives in the interval is $\lambda \delta t + \circ(\delta t)$ and so the probability that more than one customer arrives in the interval is $\circ(\delta t)$. The symbol $\circ(\delta t)$ has its usual meaning in mathematical analysis and denotes quantities which become negligible compared with δt as $\delta t \to 0$.

$$\underset{\delta t \to 0}{\text{Limit}} \frac{\circ(\delta t)}{\delta t} = 0. \tag{1.1}$$

Thus what happens in the interval $(t, t + \delta t)$ as far as arrivals are concerned is independent of t, and further is independent of any other time interval not overlapping or containing the interval $(t, t + \delta t)$. Thus the arrival or non-arrival of a customer in this interval is not influenced in any way by what has happened at earlier times.

Some important properties of this type of arrival pattern can now be derived. The definition given, essentially considers what happens in the *infinitesimal interval* $(t, t + \delta t)$. Suppose we consider the finite interval $(t, t + x)$ of length x. Then the number of arrivals in this interval of length x is a random variable N which has a Poisson distribution with parameter λx; i.e.

$$\Pr(N = n) = \frac{e^{-\lambda x}(\lambda x)^n}{n!}; \quad n = 0, 1, 2, \ldots \tag{1.2}$$

If the interval x is divided up into m equal intervals of length $\dfrac{x}{m}$ $(= \delta t)$ then as $m \to \infty$ so $\delta t \to 0$.

Now in each interval the probability that one customer arrives is $\lambda \delta t + o(\delta t)$, the probability that no customer arrives is $1 - \lambda \delta t + o(\delta t)$ and the probability of more than one customer arriving is $o(\delta t)$.

Thus the probability that exactly n customers arrive in the whole period x is given by the limiting value (as $m \to \infty$, i.e. $\delta t \to 0$) of the binomial probability

$$\Pr(N = n) = \operatorname*{Limit}_{m \to \infty} \binom{m}{n} [\lambda \delta t + o(\delta t)]^n [1 - \lambda \delta t + o(\delta t)]^{m-n}$$

$$= \operatorname*{Limit}_{m \to \infty} \frac{m(m-1)(m-2) \ldots (m-n+1)}{n!} \left(\frac{\lambda x}{m}\right)^n \left(1 - \frac{\lambda x}{m}\right)^{m-n}$$

$$= \frac{(\lambda x)^n}{n!} \cdot \operatorname*{Limit}_{m \to \infty} \frac{m}{m} \frac{(m-1)}{m} \frac{(m-2)}{m} \ldots \frac{(m-n+1)}{m} \cdot \left(1 - \frac{\lambda x}{m}\right)^m \left(1 - \frac{\lambda x}{m}\right)^{-n}.$$

Now

$$\operatorname*{Limit}_{m \to \infty} \frac{m}{m} \frac{(m-1)}{m} \frac{(m-2)}{m} \ldots \frac{(m-n+1)}{m}$$

$$= \operatorname*{Limit}_{m \to \infty} \left(1 - \frac{1}{m}\right) \left(1 - \frac{2}{m}\right) \cdots \left(1 - \frac{n-1}{m}\right) = 1;$$

$$\operatorname*{Limit}_{m \to \infty} \left(1 - \frac{\lambda x}{m}\right)^m = e^{-\lambda x} \quad \text{(the well known exponential limit)},$$

and $\operatorname*{Limit}_{m \to \infty} \left(1 - \dfrac{\lambda x}{m}\right)^{-n}$ being the finite power of a quantity which approaches 1 is itself 1.

Thus as asserted

$$\Pr(N = n) = p(n) = \frac{e^{-\lambda x}(\lambda x)^n}{n!}; \quad n = 0, 1, 2, \ldots \tag{1.3}$$

Thus N has a Poisson distribution with parameter λx. Readers will probably be familiar with the elementary properties of the Poisson distribution. For convenience a few of these properties are recorded here.

The expected value of N is

$$E\{N\} = \lambda x \tag{1.4}$$

and this is in accordance with our definition of λ as the average rate of arrivals, i.e. the average number of customers to arrive per unit time.

The variance of N is given by

$$\operatorname{Var}\{N\} = E\{N^2\} - [E\{N\}]^2$$

$$= \lambda x + (\lambda x)^2 - (\lambda x)^2$$

$$\therefore \quad \operatorname{Var}\{N\} = \lambda x = E\{N\} \tag{1.5}$$

If we apply equation (1.3) to the interval $(t, t + \delta t)$ of length δt, then we see that for this interval

$$p(0) = e^{-\lambda \delta t} = 1 - \lambda \delta t + \frac{(\lambda \delta t)^2}{2!} - \cdots$$

$$= 1 - \lambda \delta t + \circ(\delta t)$$

$$p(1) = \lambda \delta t \, e^{-\lambda \delta t} = \lambda \delta t \left[1 - \lambda \delta t + \frac{(\lambda \delta t)^2}{2!} - \cdots \right]$$

$$= \lambda \delta t + \circ(\delta t)$$

$$\Pr(N \geqslant 2) = 1 - p(0) - p(1)$$

$$= 1 - e^{-\lambda \delta t} - \lambda \delta t \, e^{-\lambda \delta t}$$

$$= \frac{(\lambda \delta t)^2}{2!} + \cdots$$

$$= \circ(\delta t)$$

in accordance with the original definition of random arrivals.

The results just derived refer to the number of customers to arrive during a given time period. It is also useful to investigate the time that elapses between the arrival of successive customers; the inter-arrival time. This will be a continuous random variable T with probability density function $f(t)$ and distribution function $F(t)$ say.

Suppose a customer arrives at a particular epoch and we measure time from this as origin. If T represents the time to the arrival of the next customer then

$$\Pr(T > t) = \Pr[\text{no customers arrive in } (0, t)]$$

$$= e^{-\lambda t}$$

by using equation (1.3) when $n = 0$.

But $\Pr(T > t) = 1 - F(t) = 1 - \Pr(T \leqslant t)$ by definition;

$$\therefore \quad F(t) = 1 - e^{-\lambda t}; \quad t \geqslant 0 \tag{1.6}$$

so that on differentiating this result

$$f(t) = \lambda \, e^{-\lambda t}; \quad t \geqslant 0. \tag{1.7}$$

As an alternative we may argue as follows:

$\Pr(t \leqslant T \leqslant t + \delta t) = f(t) \, \delta t$ to first order in δt by the definition of the probability density function.

But the event $(t \leqslant T \leqslant t + \delta t)$ is the union of the events:
no customers arrive in $(0, t)$ and 1 customer arrives in $(t, t + \delta t)$.

Thus $\Pr(t \leqslant T \leqslant t + \delta t) = e^{-\lambda t} \times \lambda \delta t$ to first order in δt, the two terms on the right coming from equation (1.3) when $n = 0$, and the definition of completely random arrivals. Thus for arbitrary small δt

$$f(t) \, \delta t = \lambda \, e^{-\lambda t} \, \delta t$$

whence

$$f(t) = \lambda \, e^{-\lambda t}; \quad t \geqslant 0 \text{ as before.}$$

Thus if customers arrive according to the random arrival pattern at average rate λ, their inter-arrival times have a negative exponential distribution with parameter λ and probability density function $\lambda e^{-\lambda t}$.

It is important to appreciate that if we choose our time origin to be an arbitrary moment in time and consider the interval that elapses until the next customer arrives then both derivations of equation (1.7) follow through exactly. Thus we can generalise the statement just made as follows: if customers arrive at random at an average rate λ, then the time that elapses from an arbitrary moment in time until the arrival of the next customer is a random variable T with probability density function $\lambda e^{-\lambda t}; t \geqslant 0$.

Again, readers with a good background in statistics and probability will be familiar with the important properties of the negative exponential distribution as given by equation (1.7). These are

$$E\{T\} = \frac{1}{\lambda}, \quad E\{T^2\} = \frac{2}{\lambda^2} \tag{1.8}$$

so that

$$\mathrm{Var}\{T\} = \frac{1}{\lambda^2} \tag{1.9}$$

In addition

$$\Pr(T \leqslant t) = 1 - e^{-\lambda t} \tag{1.10}$$

$$\Pr(T > t) = e^{-\lambda t} \tag{1.11}$$

and the Laplace Transform of $f(t)$ is

$$\mathscr{L}[f(t)] = \int_0^\infty e^{-st} f(t)\, dt$$

$$= \int_0^\infty e^{-st} \lambda e^{-\lambda t}\, dt$$

$$= \frac{\lambda}{\lambda + s} \tag{1.12}$$

If we allow the arrival pattern to be defined by equation (1.7), i.e. by the statement that inter-arrival times have a negative exponential distribution and consider the interval $(t, t + \delta t)$ where t is the time as measured from the last arrival, then:

$\Pr$(there is 1 arrival in $(t, t + \delta t)$) is the conditional probability that the inter-arrival time lies between t and $t + \delta t$ given that it is at least t.

$$\therefore \quad \Pr(\text{One arrival in } (t, t + \delta t)) = \frac{\Pr(t \leqslant T \leqslant t + \delta t)}{\Pr(T > t)}$$

$$\simeq \frac{\lambda e^{-\lambda t} \delta t}{e^{-\lambda t}} = \lambda \delta t$$

to first order in δt, which brings us back to our original definition of completely random arrivals. This probability is of course independent of t, the time since the last arrival.

Thus of the three statements:

(i) the probability of no arrivals in $(t, t + \delta t)$ is $1 - \lambda \delta t + o(\delta t)$ and the probability of one arrival in $(t, t + \delta t)$ is $\lambda \delta t + o(\delta t)$;
(ii) the number of arrivals during the interval of length x is a random variable N which has a Poisson distribution with parameter λx;
(iii) the inter-arrival time between successive customers has a negative exponential distribution with parameter λ;

we see that any one implies the other two, so that all three are essentially equivalent. Most aspects of this have been proved in the text. The reader should supply a proof for any part that he feels has not been established.

One last property of completely random arrivals is worth noting. If we consider the time that elapses until the kth customer arrives and denote this by Y_k say, then Y_k is a random variable with probability density function

$$g_k(y_k) = \frac{\lambda^k \, y_k^{k-1} \, e^{-\lambda y_k}}{(k-1)!}; \quad y_k \geqslant 0 \tag{1.13}$$

One way to establish this is by induction on k. $Y_k = T_1 + T_2 + T_3 + \cdots + T_k$ where the T_i are identically and independently distributed with the distribution given by equation (1.7). Thus, since when $k = 1$ equations (1.7) and (1.13) are identical, the result is true for the first arrival. Thus on assuming the truth of equation (1.13) for the value k, for $k + 1$ we have

$$Y_{k+1} = Y_k + T_{k+1}$$

so that

$$g_{k+1}(y_{k+1}) = \int_0^{y_{k+1}} g_k(x) \, \lambda \, e^{-\lambda(y_{k+1} - x)} \, dx; \quad y_{k+1} \geqslant 0$$

$$= \int_0^{y_{k+1}} \frac{\lambda^k \, x^{k-1} \, e^{-\lambda x}}{(k-1)!} \cdot \lambda \, e^{-\lambda(y_{k+1} - x)} \, dx$$

$$= \lambda^{k+1} \, e^{-\lambda y_{k+1}} \int_0^{y_{k+1}} \frac{x^{k-1}}{(k-1)!} \, dx$$

$$= \frac{\lambda^{k+1} \, y_{k+1}^k \, e^{-\lambda y_{k+1}}}{k!}.$$

Thus equation (1.13) holds for the next value of k and so for all values of k.

A simpler approach which more readily links up with the Poisson distribution for the number of arrivals in a given time is to consider the distribution function for Y_k.

$$G_k(y_k) = \Pr(Y_k \leqslant y_k) = \Pr(\text{at least } k \text{ arrivals in } (0, y_k))$$

$$= 1 - \sum_{r=0}^{k-1} \frac{e^{-\lambda y_k} (\lambda y_k)^r}{r!}.$$

If we differentiate this to obtain the density function all but one of the terms cancel and we obtain

$$g_k(y_k) = \frac{\lambda^k \, y_k^{k-1} \, e^{-\lambda y_k}}{(k-1)!}$$

as before and in accordance with equation (1.13).

It has already been mentioned that completely random arrivals were used to model the arrival of calls at a telephone exchange. This is reasonable, for if we consider a time interval of length x (from 10.30 a.m. to 11.00 a.m. for example) and the number of calls to the exchange in this interval, then of the very large number of subscribers (n) who could call the exchange we must realise that any individual will have a very small probability (p) of calling the exchange in the interval. Thus we have a classic situation whereby the number of calls which has a binomial distribution $B(n, p)$ is adequately approximated by a Poisson distribution with parameter np (assumed finite). In view of earlier remarks this justifies the use of a random arrival pattern. More generally the random arrival pattern is likely to be appropriate in situations where the arrivals stem from the independent behaviour of a large number of potential customers.

Of course in the example just mentioned the average rate of arrivals may vary with the time of day, being greater during the period 10.30 a.m. to 11.00 a.m. than say 11.00 p.m. to 11.30 p.m. These non-stationary patterns will not generally be considered in the first course covered in this book, although it is clear that they do arise in this and other situations.

We found in the discussion of completely random arrivals that a convenient way to describe the arrival pattern was through a description of the inter-arrival time. If these times are independent for successive customers and have a general distribution function $G(t)$ then we have *general independent arrivals*. If $G(t)$ has the form

$$G(t) = 1 - e^{-\lambda t}$$

then we have completely random arrivals; if $G(t)$ corresponds to a discrete distribution concentrated at a value c, so that $G(t) = 0$, $t < c$; $G(t) = 1$ for $t \geq c$; i.e. $G(t) = H(t - c)$ where $H(x)$ is the Heaviside unit step function then we have regular arrivals at intervals of time of duration c.

General independent arrivals can clearly be used to model a wide variety of situations although equally it is clear that this will *not* cover all cases. As readers progress beyond this present text they will have occasion to study more advanced and specialised models. We shall not have time or space at the moment to consider these.

1.4   The Service Mechanism

Two important aspects of the service mechanism which are needed to model it, are the capacity, in terms of the number of customers that can be served at any one time, and the times when the service is available. In our models we shall assume that the service facility is always available but we shall study in turn single-server queues, two-server queues, ..., m-server queues and indeed self-service queues in which the number of servers is the same as the number of customers whatever the latter.

Finally we shall need to consider the duration of service time, i.e. the time taken for a server to serve a customer. A fairly wide range of models derive from the assumption that this is a random variable X whose distribution does not change in time and that the service times of successive customers are statistically independent. Thus we may specify a general independent service time distribution $G(x)$.

$$G(x) = H(x - b) \tag{1.14}$$

would correspond to constant service time of duration b. If it is reasonable to assume that the service time has a negative exponential distribution with probability density function

$$g(x) = \mu\, e^{-\mu x}, \quad x \geqslant 0 \tag{1.15}$$

$$G(x) = 1 - e^{-\mu x}, \quad x \geqslant 0 \tag{1.16}$$

then our models become easier to handle mathematically. This is a consequence of a certain property of this service time distribution.

The mean and variance of this service time distribution are $1/\mu$ and $1/\mu^2$ respectively as is well known.

$$E\{X\} = \frac{1}{\mu}; \quad \mathrm{Var}\{X\} = \frac{1}{\mu^2}. \tag{1.17}$$

Also

$$\Pr(X > x) = e^{-\mu x}. \tag{1.18}$$

Thus the probability that the service of a customer finishes in the interval $(x, x + \delta x)$, given that it has already been in progress for time x is the conditional probability

$$\Pr(x \leqslant X \leqslant x + \delta x \,|\, X \geqslant x) \simeq \frac{g(x)\,\delta x}{\Pr(X \geqslant x)}$$

by definition of the probability density function.

Thus in the case of negative exponential service times the probability that a service which has been in progress for time x, terminates in the interval $(x, x + \delta x)$ is

$$\frac{\mu\, e^{-\mu x}\, \delta x}{e^{-\mu x}} = \mu \delta x \quad \text{to first order in } \delta x, \tag{1.19}$$

and this is independent of x. It is from this property that the mathematical simplicity derives. For any other distribution of service time the probability that the service finishes in an interval $(x, x + \delta x)$ will also depend on x, the time for which the service has been in progress. The probability that the service does not finish in the interval $(x, x + \delta x)$ is

$$1 - \mu \delta x \quad \text{to first order in } \delta x. \tag{1.20}$$

One observes that there is an analogy between random arrivals, where the inter-arrival time has a negative exponential distribution, and negative exponential service times where the probability for the completion or non-completion of service in an interval $(x, x + \delta x)$ is given by equations (1.19) and (1.20) respectively.

It follows, and the proof is identical to the derivation of equation (1.3), that in the case of negative exponential service times, *provided service is going on all the time*, the number N of customers to be served during the interval $(t, t + x)$ has a Poisson distribution and

$$\Pr(N = n) = \frac{e^{-\mu x}(\mu x)^n}{n!}; \quad n = 0, 1, 2, \ldots \tag{1.21}$$

It is not only from the mathematical simplicity of the negative exponential distribution as a service time model, that its importance derives. It is indeed a good representation of the duration of telephone calls as experimental observations on the latter have indicated. From equations (1.17) we see that its mean and standard deviation are equal so that it has a relatively large spread of values compared to its mean. It is often a good approximation in situations in which there is a large range of values, with a few customers requiring long service times and a much larger number requiring short service times, as at a doctor's surgery perhaps?

In concluding this section it is useful to introduce a shorthand notation to describe a queueing system. This consists of specifying the inter-arrival time distribution (M ≡ negative exponential, (actually M for Markovian), D ≡ a constant (D for Deterministic), G ≡ general independent), the service time distribution and the number of servers, the three elements being separated by slashes. Thus:

M/M/1 denotes a single-server queue with random arrivals (negative exponential inter-arrival time) and negative exponential service time;

D/G/2 denotes a two-server queue with regular arrivals (constant inter-arrival time) and a general independent distribution of service times. Occasionally this notation contains suitable adornments to indicate that customers arrive in groups or that there is limited waiting room.

1.5   Random Arrivals Again

Random arrivals and negative exponential service will play a major role in the models to be discussed in this book, and no excuse is made for returning to the subject. The result (1.3) is now derived in a different but instructive manner and the technique involved is one that the student of queueing theory should master.

Thus we suppose that customers arrive at random at average rate λ so that

$$\Pr(\text{no customers arrive in } (t, t + \delta t)) = 1 - \lambda \delta t + o(\delta t), \tag{1.22}$$

$$\Pr(1 \text{ customer arrives in } (t, t + \delta t)) = \lambda \delta t + o(\delta t), \tag{1.23}$$

$$\Pr(\text{more than 1 customer arrives in } (t, t + \delta t)) = o(\delta t). \tag{1.24}$$

We do not consider any service mechanism at the moment but assume that customers who arrive simply congregate in some waiting area. Thus the *state* of the system at any time t will be adequately described by the number of customers who have arrived by time t. This will of course be a random variable and we let $p_n(t)$ denote the probability that there are n customers in the system at time t. If we start with an empty system at time zero then

$$p_n(0) = 0; \quad n \neq 0: \quad p_0(0) = 1. \tag{1.25}$$

Consider the interval $(t, t + \delta t)$, and the way in which the system must change to reach the final state.

If there are no customers at time $t + \delta t$, then this can only arise from there being no customers at time t and no arrivals in $(t, t + \delta t)$;

i.e. $$p_0(t + \delta t) = p_0(t)(1 - \lambda \delta t + \circ(\delta t)). \qquad (1.26)$$

If there is one customer at time $t + \delta t$, then this can arise in two ways. Either at time t there were no customers and there was an arrival in $(t, t + \delta t)$, or at time t there was one customer and there were no arrivals in $(t, t + \delta t)$

i.e. $$p_1(t + \delta t) = p_0(t)(\lambda \delta t + \circ(\delta t)) + p_1(t)(1 - \lambda \delta t + \circ(\delta t)). \qquad (1.27)$$

The same argument used to derive equation (1.27) shows that quite generally for $n \geqslant 1$

$$p_n(t + \delta t) = p_{n-1}(t)(\lambda \delta t + \circ(\delta t)) + p_n(t)(1 - \lambda \delta t + \circ(\delta t)). \qquad (1.28)$$

Thus if we rearrange these equations we obtain

$$\frac{p_0(t + \delta t) - p_0(t)}{\delta t} = -\lambda p_0(t) + \frac{\circ(\delta t)}{\delta t}$$

$$\frac{p_1(t + \delta t) - p_1(t)}{\delta t} = \lambda p_0(t) - \lambda p_1(t) + \frac{\circ(\delta t)}{\delta t} \qquad (1.29)$$

and for $n > 1$ $$\frac{p_n(t + \delta t) - p_n(t)}{\delta t} = \lambda p_{n-1}(t) - \lambda p_n(t) + \frac{\circ(\delta t)}{\delta t}$$

Thus as $\delta t \to 0$ we obtain the system of differential equations

$$\frac{dp_0(t)}{dt} = \qquad -\lambda p_0(t)$$

$$\frac{dp_1(t)}{dt} = \lambda p_0(t) - \lambda p_1(t) \qquad (1.30)$$

$$- - - - - - - - - - - -$$

$$\frac{dp_n(t)}{dt} = \lambda p_{n-1}(t) - \lambda p_n(t)$$

etc.

We have to solve this infinite set of equations subject to the initial conditions (1.25). One way to find a solution to these equations is to use the generating function

$$\pi(t, z) = \sum_{n=0}^{\infty} p_n(t) z^n \qquad (1.31)$$

for the $p_n(t)$.

Multiplication of the equations in (1.30) by $z^0, z^1, z^2, \ldots, z^n \ldots$ followed by addition gives

$$\sum_{n=0}^{\infty} \frac{dp_n(t)}{dt} \cdot z^n = \lambda z \sum_{n=0}^{\infty} p_n(t) z^n - \lambda \sum_{n=0}^{\infty} p_n(t) z^n$$

$$\therefore \quad \frac{\partial \pi}{\partial t}(t, z) = \lambda(z - 1) \pi(t, z). \qquad (1.32)$$

Thus we have transformed the set of simultaneous ordinary differential equations (1.30) into the partial differential equation (1.32). This equation is easily solved, indeed

$$\pi(t, z) = C\, e^{\lambda(z-1)t} \tag{1.33}$$

where C is a constant in time. It could be a function of z. In terms of $\pi(t, z)$ the conditions (1.25) become

$$\pi(0, z) = 1 \tag{1.34}$$

so that $C = 1$ and

$$\pi(t, z) = e^{\lambda(z-1)t} = e^{-\lambda t}\, e^{\lambda t z}. \tag{1.35}$$

Thus if we expand this as a power series in z we obtain

$$\pi(t, z) = e^{-\lambda t}\left[1 + \lambda t z + \frac{(\lambda t)^2}{2!} z^2 + \frac{(\lambda t)^3}{3!} z^3 + \cdots\right]$$

whence

$$p_n(t) = \frac{e^{-\lambda t}(\lambda t)^n}{n!}; \quad \text{the coefficient of } z^n. \tag{1.36}$$

This of course is the same result as equation (1.3).

Exercises 1

1 A random variable N has a Poisson distribution with parameter α so that $\Pr(N = n) = \dfrac{e^{-\alpha}\alpha^n}{n!}$, $n = 0, 1, 2, \ldots$. Show that $E\{N\} = \text{Var}\{N\} = \alpha$. Show also that the probability generating function for this distribution is

$$E\{z^N\} = e^{\alpha(z-1)}.$$

2 A random variable T has a negative exponential distribution with probability density function

$$f(t) = \lambda\, e^{-\lambda t}; \quad t \geqslant 0.$$

Show by direct integration that
(i) $E\{T\} = \dfrac{1}{\lambda}$. (ii) $\text{Var}\{T\} = \dfrac{1}{\lambda^2}$. (iii) The coefficient of variation ($=$ standard deviation/mean) $= 1$. (iv) $E\{T^n\} = \dfrac{\Gamma(n+1)}{\lambda^n} = \dfrac{n!}{\lambda^n}$ (if n is an integer).

Verify the last result by showing that the Laplace transform of the density is $\dfrac{\lambda}{\lambda + s}$ and expanding this function.

3 We have seen that for random arrivals at average rate λ, the time to the kth arrival, $Y_k = T_1 + T_2 + \cdots + T_k$, where the inter-arrival times T_i are identically and independently distributed with probability density function $\lambda e^{-\lambda t}$.

Show that the Laplace transform of the probability density function for Y_k is $\left(\dfrac{\lambda}{\lambda+s}\right)^k$ by using the form for Y_k just given.

Verify by direct integration that the Laplace transform of the density function

$$g(y) = \frac{\lambda^k\, y^{k-1}\, e^{-\lambda y}}{(k-1)!}\,; \quad y \geqslant 0$$

is also $\left(\dfrac{\lambda}{\lambda+s}\right)^k$ and hence establish equation (1.13).

4   A family of distributions closely allied to that discussed in Question 3 are the Erlang distributions. The kth Erlang distribution ($\equiv E_k$ in the notation of Section 1.4) has probability density function

$$f(x) = \frac{1}{(k-1)!}\, k\mu(k\mu x)^{k-1}\, e^{-k\mu x}\,; \quad x \geqslant 0,$$

and contains two parameters $\mu > 0$ and $k = 1, 2, 3, \ldots$.
   Show that if X has density function $f(x)$ then

$$E\{X\} = \frac{1}{\mu} \quad \text{and} \quad \text{Var}\{X\} = \frac{1}{k\mu^2}.$$

Verify that $k = 1$ corresponds to the negative exponential distribution, and $k \to \infty$ corresponds to a constant distribution for $X\left(=\dfrac{1}{\mu}\right).\left[X \text{ can be considered as the sum}\right.$ of k independent random variables each having a negative exponential distribution with mean $\left.\dfrac{1}{k\mu}.\right]$

5   Suppose customers arrive at a waiting area at random at an average rate λ. Suppose that initially there are i customers in the waiting area. If $p_n(t)$ denotes the probability that there are n customers in the area at time t show that

$$p_n(t) = \frac{e^{-\lambda t}(\lambda t)^{n-i}}{(n-i)!}.$$

6   Suppose that arrivals to a waiting area occur at unit time intervals but that an arrival corresponds not to a single customer but to a group of N customers where N is a random variable with mean μ and variance σ^2. Find the mean and variance of the number of customers in the area at time t. If N has a Poisson distribution what is the distribution of the total number in the area at time t?

7   Arrivals to a waiting area from one source occur at random at average rate λ_1 and from a second independent source at random at rate λ_2. Show that the overall pattern of arrivals is random at rate $\lambda_1 + \lambda_2$.

8   Cars on a trunk road pass by a petrol station at random at an average rate λ. A proportion q of the passing cars call at the station for petrol or service etc. Show that, provided the cars behave independently, customers to the station will arrive randomly at an average rate λq.

9 Service times have a negative exponential distribution with density function $\mu e^{-\mu x}$; $x \geqslant 0$. If service has been in progress for time t, show that the probability that it does not finish in the interval $(t, t + \delta t)$ is $1 - \mu \delta t + o(\delta t)$.

10 Show that if a distribution with density function $f(x)$ and distribution function $F(x)$ is such that $\dfrac{f(x)}{1 - F(x)} = \mu$ where μ is a constant [see the derivation of equation (1.19)] then $f(x) = \mu e^{-\mu x}$.

11 Service times have a distribution such that when the service has been in progress for time t, the time that remains until the service is completed has a distribution which is independent of t. Show that the service time has a negative exponential distribution.

12 Let X_1, X_2, ..., X_n be the n values in a random sample from a uniform distribution over the range $(0, t)$ with probability density function

$$f(x) = \frac{1}{t}, \quad 0 \leqslant x \leqslant t.$$

Show that the joint density function

$$f(x_1, x_2, \ldots, x_n) = \frac{1}{t^n}; \quad 0 \leqslant x_i \leqslant t.$$

If Y_1, Y_2, ..., Y_n are the sample values in ascending magnitude $0 \leqslant Y_1 \leqslant Y_2 \leqslant \ldots$, $Y_n \leqslant t$ then Y_1, Y_2, ..., Y_n are called the order statistics of the sample.
Show that their joint density function is

$$f(y_1, y_2, \ldots, y_n) = \frac{n!}{t^n}, \quad 0 \leqslant y_1 \leqslant y_2 \leqslant \cdots \leqslant y_n \leqslant t.$$

13 For a system of random arrivals at average rate λ, let the time of the nth arrival be denoted by Y_n. Suppose it is known that $Y_{n+1} = t$. Show that the conditional joint density for Y_1, Y_2, ..., Y_n is

$$f(y_1, y_2, \ldots, y_n | t) = \frac{n!}{t^n}; \quad 0 \leqslant y_1 \leqslant y_2 \leqslant \cdots \leqslant y_n \leqslant t.$$

Thus the successive arrival times have the same distribution as the order statistics of a random sample of n values from the uniform distribution on the range $(0, t)$.

14 Sequel to Question 13. Suppose it is known that exactly n arrivals have occurred by time t. Show once again that the conditional joint density for Y_1, Y_2, ..., Y_n is

$$f(y_1, y_2, \ldots, y_n | t) = \frac{n!}{t^n}; \quad 0 \leqslant y_1 \leqslant y_2 \leqslant \cdots \leqslant y_n \leqslant t.$$

The results established in Questions 13 and 14 may help to explain the term 'random arrivals' for this particular pattern. Given that n customers have arrived by time t, their arrival times, when unordered are uniformly and independently distributed on $(0, t)$.

15   Suppose customers arrive at random at an average rate $\lambda(t)$ at time t, i.e. the arrival rate is a function of time. Use the method of Section 1.5 to show that if we start with an empty system then the probability of n arrivals by time t is

$$\frac{\mu^n e^{-\mu}}{n!} \quad \text{where} \quad \mu = \int_0^t \lambda(u)\, \mathrm{d}u.$$

If $\lambda(t) = \alpha e^{-\beta t}$ show that the probability that no customers arrive in the interval (u, v) is

$$\exp\left\{ -\frac{\alpha}{\beta}\left(e^{-\beta u} - e^{-\beta v}\right) \right\}.$$

16   If the service time X has probability density function $f(x)$ and distribution function $F(x)$ show that the mean service time

$$E\{X\} = \int_0^\infty x f(x)\, \mathrm{d}x = \int_0^\infty (1 - F(x))\, \mathrm{d}x.$$

17   If the service time X, with probability density function $f(x)$ and distribution function $F(x)$, is such that

$$\Pr(x \leqslant X \leqslant x + \delta x \,|\, X \geqslant x) = g(x)\, \delta x$$

to first order in δx (see the derivation of equation (1.19) and also Question 10 of these exercises) then $g(x)$ is referred to as the instantaneous rate of completion of service when service has been proceeding for time x. Show that

$$F(x) = 1 - \exp\left\{ -\int_0^x g(u)\, \mathrm{d}u \right\}$$

$$f(x) = g(x) \exp\left\{ -\int_0^x g(u)\, \mathrm{d}u \right\}.$$

2
The M/M/1 Queue

2.1 A Very Simple System

In Chapter 1 some simple properties of random arrivals and negative exponential service times were derived. We did not however consider queues, where both processes are going on simultaneously. Of course even in a queueing system this is not necessarily so all of the time. Service will not be taking place unless there are customers in the system requiring to be served.

Consider the following situation. An operator is in charge of an automatic machine which produces some product. From time to time the machine breaks down and needs to be repaired. When this occurs the operator carries out the repair and sets the machine running again until it next fails and so on. This can be viewed as a very simple queueing system. Whilst the machine is running it is a *potential customer* to the queue. When it breaks down it 'arrives' and is promptly 'serviced', i.e. repaired by the operator and on completion of the repair it again becomes a potential customer. For this problem there is no delay between arrival and the commencement of service, because there is never more than one customer in the system.

We can give a description of the system at any time by specifying the state of the machine. The machine is either running (state R) or stopped, being repaired (state S). Before we can go any further in our analysis we shall need more details of the running times of the machine, i.e. the length of time from the completion of a repair until the next breakdown, and the time spent on a repair (the service time). We shall assume that the running times have a negative exponential distribution with mean $1/\lambda$, and the repair times have a negative exponential distribution with mean $1/\mu$ where λ and μ are known constants. Thus from the properties of random arrivals and exponential service we see that if the machine is running at time t, the probability that it will still be running at time $t + \delta t$ is $1 - \lambda \delta t + \circ(\delta t)$ and the probability that it will be stopped at time $t + \delta t$ is $\lambda \delta t + \circ(\delta t)$. Further we see that if the machine is being repaired at time t, the probability that the repair is still going on at time $t + \delta t$ is $1 - \mu \delta t + \circ(\delta t)$, whereas the probability that it is completed by time $t + \delta t$ is $\mu \delta t + \circ(\delta t)$. Thus if in order to give a stochastic description of the system we let

$$\left. \begin{array}{l} p_R(t) \equiv \text{Probability the machine is running at time } t \\ p_S(t) \equiv \text{Probability the machine is stopped at time } t \end{array} \right\} \tag{2.1}$$

then we obtain

$$p_R(t + \delta t) = p_R(t)(1 - \lambda \delta t + \circ(\delta t)) + p_S(t)(\mu \delta t + \circ(\delta t)) \tag{2.2}$$

$$p_S(t + \delta t) = p_R(t)(\lambda \delta t + \circ(\delta t)) + p_S(t)(1 - \mu \delta t + \circ(\delta t)). \tag{2.3}$$

For equation (2.2), the machine is running at $t + \delta t$ if it is running at t and does not break down in $(t, t + \delta t)$, or it is stopped at time t and the ongoing repair is completed in $(t, t + \delta t)$. For equation (2.3), the machine is stopped at $t + \delta t$, if it is running at time t and fails in $(t, t + \delta t)$ or it is stopped at time t and the ongoing repair is not completed in $(t, t + \delta t)$.

A little manipulation of equations (2.2) and (2.3) gives

$$\frac{p_R(t + \delta t) - p_R(t)}{\delta t} = -\lambda p_R(t) + \mu p_S(t) + \frac{o(\delta t)}{\delta t}$$

$$\frac{p_S(t + \delta t) - p_S(t)}{\delta t} = \lambda p_R(t) - \mu p_S(t) + \frac{o(\delta t)}{\delta t}$$

so that as $\delta t \to 0$

$$\frac{dp_R(t)}{dt} = -\lambda p_R(t) + \mu p_S(t) \tag{2.4}$$

$$\frac{dp_S(t)}{dt} = \lambda p_R(t) - \mu p_S(t) \tag{2.5}$$

Of course

$$p_R(t) + p_S(t) = 1. \tag{2.6}$$

From the addition of equations (2.4) and (2.5)

$$\frac{d}{dt}(p_R(t) + p_S(t)) = 0$$

so that $p_R(t) + p_S(t)$ is clearly a constant and of course that constant is 1.

Thus we have derived a pair of differential equations for the probabilities $p_R(t)$ and $p_S(t)$. If we use equation (2.6) to eliminate $p_S(t)$ from equation (2.4) we readily obtain

$$\frac{dp_R(t)}{dt} = \mu - (\lambda + \mu) p_R(t). \tag{2.7}$$

This has general solution

$$p_R(t) = \frac{\mu}{\lambda + \mu} + A e^{-(\lambda + \mu)t}. \tag{2.8}$$

Thus if when $t = 0$, $p_R(t) = p_R(0)$, (we know the state of the machine at the outset, in a stochastic sense at least), then

$$p_R(t) = \frac{\mu}{\lambda + \mu} [1 - e^{-(\lambda + \mu)t}] + p_R(0) e^{-(\lambda + \mu)t}. \tag{2.9}$$

Similarly

$$p_S(t) = \frac{\lambda}{\lambda + \mu} [1 - e^{-(\lambda + \mu)t}] + p_S(0) e^{-(\lambda + \mu)t}. \tag{2.10}$$

Equations (2.9) and (2.10) provide the time-dependent solution (transient solution) for the system and give a stochastic description of the state of the system at any time t.

For this problem it is easy to deduce the steady-state (equilibrium) solution. As $t \to \infty$, $p_R(t) \to p_R$, where

$$p_R = \underset{t \to \infty}{\text{Limit }} p_R(t) = \frac{\mu}{\lambda + \mu},$$ (2.11)

$$p_S = \underset{t \to \infty}{\text{Limit }} p_S(t) = \frac{\lambda}{\lambda + \mu}.$$ (2.12)

Thus after a long time, the probability that at any instant we find the machine running is p_R and the probability that we find it stopped is p_S. These probabilities for the steady-state solution are reached after a long time no matter how the system starts. They are independent of $p_R(0)$ and $p_S(0)$.

Of course, if we are prepared to accept that a steady-state solution to equations (2.4), (2.5) and (2.6) exists, then a simpler way in which to obtain this solution is as follows. If $\underset{t \to \infty}{\text{limit }} p_R(t) = p_R$ and $\underset{t \to \infty}{\text{limit }} p_S(t) = p_S$ then also $\underset{t \to \infty}{\text{limit }} \dfrac{\mathrm{d}p_R(t)}{\mathrm{d}t} = 0$ and $\underset{t \to \infty}{\text{limit }} \dfrac{\mathrm{d}p_S(t)}{\mathrm{d}t} = 0$. Hence we deduce from (2.4), (2.5) and (2.6) that

$$0 = -\lambda p_R + \mu p_S$$

$$0 = \lambda p_R - \mu p_S$$

and

$$1 = p_R + p_S$$

whence

$$p_R = \frac{\mu}{\lambda + \mu} \quad \text{and} \quad p_S = \frac{\lambda}{\lambda + \mu}$$ (2.13)

as before.

If we start the system in the steady state so that

$$p_R(0) = p_R, \quad p_S(0) = p_S$$

then from equations (2.9) and (2.10)

$$p_R(t) = \frac{\mu}{\lambda + \mu} = p_R$$

and

$$p_S(t) = \frac{\lambda}{\lambda + \mu} = p_S.$$

From these results it is clear that if once the system reaches its steady state it will remain in this state thereafter. One further property of the steady-state solution for this system is worth noting. It is possible to represent the state of the system over time, on a diagram, as in Fig. 2.1.

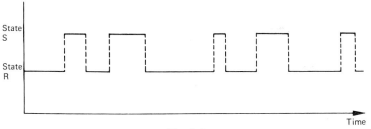

Fig. 2.1

Here we have represented the passage of time across the page and have indicated by the continuous line whether the machine is running (in state R) or stopped (in state S) at any time. We have supposed for the purposes of our illustration that the machine starts running. When it breaks down it jumps from state R to state S and on completion of the repair back to state R again. These successive transitions between the two states continue through time. The periods it spends in state R will be random sample values from a negative exponential distribution with mean $1/\lambda$. The periods spent in state S will be random sample values from a negative exponential distribution with mean $1/\mu$. If we consider $2N$ transitions where N is very large, the total time spent in state R will be the sum of N independent negative exponential variables and will asymptotically be N/λ. Similarly the total time spent in state S will asymptotically be N/μ.

Thus the long run proportion of time spent in state R is

$$\frac{\dfrac{N}{\lambda}}{\dfrac{N}{\lambda}+\dfrac{N}{\mu}} = \frac{\mu}{\lambda+\mu} = p_R \tag{2.14}$$

and the long run proportion of time spent in state S is

$$\frac{\dfrac{N}{\mu}}{\dfrac{N}{\lambda}+\dfrac{N}{\mu}} = \frac{\lambda}{\lambda+\mu} = p_S. \tag{2.15}$$

Thus the long run proportion of time the machine is running is p_R, and the proportion of time for which it is stopped is p_S. This is a somewhat different interpretation of the steady-state probabilities as the probability that at an arbitrary instant in time we find the machine running (or stopped) after a long time has elapsed.

Example 1

An operative is in charge of a machine that automatically twists insulated wires together to make a telephone cable. From time to time problems occur which call for manual intervention. Studies over a period of several weeks indicate that such difficulties occur at random at an average rate of 1 per hour of actual running time. The time taken for the operative to correct the problem has an exponential distribution with a mean of 15 minutes. Find the average amount of actual production time during an 8 hour shift. The cable making is run as a continuous process 24 hours each day.

The final statement suggests that after a long time the state of the machine will be reasonably described by the steady-state probabilities as given by equations (2.11) and (2.12) and their other interpretation in the form of equations (2.14) and (2.15).
In this problem with the time units in hours

$$\lambda = 1 \text{ breakdown/hour}, \quad \mu = 4 \text{ repairs/hour}.$$

$$\therefore \quad p_R = \frac{4}{1+4} = \frac{4}{5}$$

so that in 8 hours we might expect to get $32/5 = 6.4$ actual production hours.
It also follows that the operative is only working at this task for 1.6 hours, so that it would seem sensible to arrange for him to have other tasks which he can perform, and break off from, when he is required to repair the cable making machine. Of course it could be that it is even more sensible to give him several cable making machines to look after but that is another story that we shall take up later (see Chapter 5).

2.2   Some Properties of the M/M/1 Queue

In this section we shall investigate some properties of the single-server queue (with a first come first served queue discipline) in which it is assumed that the customers arrive at random at an average rate λ and that their service times have a negative exponential distribution with mean $1/\mu$. An alternative way of expressing the latter assumption is to say that service is exponential at rate μ. Both λ and μ are assumed to be constants which are known.

Before embarking on a quantitative analysis of this system it might be useful to make one or two general remarks of a qualitative nature. We can give a diagrammatic representation of the system at any time t as in Figures 2.2(a) and 2.2(b). In Fig. 2.2(a) there are 4 customers *in the system*, including the one being served, (in the service box). There are 3 customers *in the queue*, i.e. waiting for service. In Fig. 2.2(b) the system is empty.

x   x   x | x | □

Fig. 2.2(a)   **Fig. 2.2(b)**

In general, at time t, the number of customers in the system will be a random variable $N(t)$ whose value will depend on t. Provided $N(t) \geq 1$ the number in the queue, $Q(t)$, will be $N(t) - 1$, but if $N(t) = 0$ then $Q(t) = 0$ also. We shall be careful to draw this distinction between customers in the system and customers in the queue.
$N(t)$ will be increased by 1 with the arrival of a customer and will decrease by 1 with each service completion. We state the obvious; there cannot be a service completion

unless there is at least one customer in the system. Thus there is a difference between the arrival and service processes. The former is always going on but there can be no service unless there are customers to serve. Thus we can give a diagrammatic representation of the state of the system, $N(t)$ as a function of t as in Fig. 2.3.

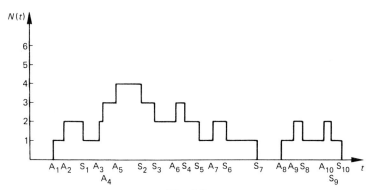

Fig. 2.3

$A_1, A_2, A_3, \ldots$ etc. correspond to the times of the first, second, third, $\ldots$ arrivals. $S_1, S_2, \ldots$ etc. correspond to the service completion times of the first, second, $\ldots$ customers. The server starts serving at time A_1 and is kept busy until time S_7. He is then idle until time A_8 and then busy until time S_{10}. (A_1, S_7) constitutes a *busy period* for the server, as does (A_8, S_{10}), whereas (S_7, A_8) constitutes an *idle period*.

Of course as it stands Fig. 2.3 is a representation of the G/G/1 queue rather than the M/M/1 queue. It will represent the latter if the intervals (A_i, A_{i+1}) are sample values from a negative exponential distribution with mean $1/\lambda$, to represent random arrivals, and the service times are sample values from a negative exponential distribution with mean $1/\mu$. Note that the service times for the successive customers are represented by the intervals $(A_1, S_1), (S_1, S_2), \ldots, (S_6, S_7)$ [at which time the first busy period ends], $(A_8, S_8), (S_8, S_9), (S_9, S_{10})$ etc. Thus although all inter-arrival times are represented by intervals of the kind (A_i, A_{i+1}) NOT ALL service times are represented by intervals of the kind (S_i, S_{i+1}). Those that occur at the start of a busy period are represented by intervals of the form (A_i, S_i).

In the case of the M/M/1 queue the changes that occur in $N(t)$ during the interval $(t, t+\delta t)$ are governed by the properties of random arrivals and negative exponential service as given by equations (1.22), (1.23), and (1.24) and (1.19) and (1.20). Thus if we proceed in the manner of Section 1.5 and let $p_n(t)$ be the probability that $N(t) = n$, i.e. that there are n customers in the system at time t then to first order in δt

$$p_0(t + \delta t) = p_0(t)(1 - \lambda \delta t + \circ(\delta t)) + p_1(t)(1 - \lambda \delta t + \circ(\delta t))(\mu \delta t + \circ(\delta t)) \quad (2.16)$$

$$p_1(t + \delta t) = p_0(t)(\lambda \delta t + \circ(\delta t)) + p_1(t)(1 - \mu \delta t + \circ(\delta t))(1 - \lambda \delta t + \circ(\delta t))$$

$$+ p_2(t)(\mu \delta t + \circ(\delta t))(1 - \lambda \delta t + \circ(\delta t)) \quad (2.17)$$

and for $n \geq 2$

$$p_n(t + \delta t) = p_{n-1}(t)(\lambda \delta t + \circ(\delta t))(1 - \mu \delta t + \circ(\delta t))$$

$$+ p_n(t)(1 - \lambda \delta t + \circ(\delta t))(1 - \mu \delta t + \circ(\delta t))$$

$$+ p_{n+1}(t)(1 - \lambda \delta t + \circ(\delta t))(\mu \delta t + \circ(\delta t)). \qquad (2.18)$$

For equation (2.16) the system will have no customers at $t + \delta t$, if there were no customers at time t and no arrivals in the interval $(t, t + \delta t)$, or there was 1 customer at time t whose service is completed in $(t, t + \delta t)$ whilst no other customers arrive in this interval. The probability that $N(t)$ increases or decreases by 2 or more is $\circ(\delta t)$ and so these situations are not included in any of equations (2.16), (2.17) or (2.18). For equation (2.18) a similar argument holds. Three mutually exclusive situations give rise to the event, n customers in the system at time $t + \delta t$. These are: $(n-1)$ in the system at time t with an arrival but no service completion in $(t, t + \delta t)$; n in the system at time t with no arrivals or service completion in $(t, t + \delta t)$; $n+1$ in the system at time t with a service completion but no arrivals in $(t, t + \delta t)$.

A little manipulation of these equations gives

$$\frac{p_0(t + \delta t) - p_0(t)}{\delta t} = \qquad -\lambda p_0(t) \qquad + \mu p_1(t) \quad + \frac{\circ(\delta t)}{\delta t}$$

$$\frac{p_1(t + \delta t) - p_1(t)}{\delta t} = \lambda p_0(t) \quad - (\lambda + \mu) p_1(t) + \mu p_2(t) \quad + \frac{\circ(\delta t)}{\delta t}$$

$$- -$$

$$\frac{p_n(t + \delta t) - p_n(t)}{\delta t} = \lambda p_{n-1}(t) - (\lambda + \mu) p_n(t) + \mu p_{n+1}(t) + \frac{\circ(\delta t)}{\delta t}$$

etc.

Thus as $\delta t \to 0$ we obtain the set of simultaneous equations for $p_0(t), p_1(t), \ldots, p_n(t) \ldots$ as given:

$$\left. \begin{array}{l} \dfrac{\mathrm{d}p_0(t)}{\mathrm{d}t} = \qquad\qquad -\lambda p_0(t) \qquad + \mu p_1(t) \\[2ex] \dfrac{\mathrm{d}p_1(t)}{\mathrm{d}t} = \quad \lambda p_0(t) - (\lambda + \mu) p_1(t) + \mu p_2(t) \\[2ex] \dfrac{\mathrm{d}p_2(t)}{\mathrm{d}t} = \quad \lambda p_1(t) - (\lambda + \mu) p_2(t) + \mu p_3(t) \\[2ex] - - - - - - - - - - - - - - - - - \\[1ex] \dfrac{\mathrm{d}p_n(t)}{\mathrm{d}t} = \lambda p_{n-1}(t) - (\lambda + \mu) p_n(t) + \mu p_{n+1}(t) \end{array} \right\} \qquad (2.19)$$

etc.

Our problem is to find a solution to equations (2.19) subject to some initial conditions. For example if we know that the system is empty at time zero we should have $p_0(0) = 1$, $p_n(0) = 0$ for $n \neq 0$. Unfortunately equations (2.19) are not easy to solve. These equations were written down by Erlang before 1920. They were not solved until 1952 which gives some idea of the scale of the problem. It is perhaps worth emphasising at this stage that the equations we have derived are only appropriate to the random arrivals exponential service problem. It is only in this case that the probabilities of an arrival or a service completion in the interval $(t, t + \delta t)$ are independent of t and so it is only for this case that equations (2.16), (2.17) and (2.18) are valid.

We have already mentioned the difficulties involved in solving equations (2.19). However, we might ask if we can find a steady-state solution if one exists. Intuitively we might expect this to be the case if the arrival rate is less than the service rate. Certainly if the arrival rate is greater than the service rate we would expect the number of customers in the system to grow without limit and this indeed is the case. A rigorous investigation of the equations (2.19) is beyond the scope of this book and we shall simply note the result that a steady-state solution exists if $\lambda < \mu$. This follows from the work of Karlin and McGregor and Reuter. There are of course two ways to find the steady-state solution. The hard way is to find $p_n(t)$ (very hard indeed) and investigate $\lim_{t \to \infty} p_n(t) = p_n$. The easy way is to proceed as in Section 2.1 by noting that

if $\lim_{t \to \infty} p_n(t) = p_n$ then also $\lim_{t \to \infty} \dfrac{dp_n(t)}{dt} = 0$.

Thus for the steady-state probabilities p_n, we have from equations (2.19))

$$0 = \qquad\qquad -\lambda p_0 + \mu p_1$$
$$0 = \lambda p_0 \quad -(\lambda + \mu)\, p_1 + \mu p_2$$
$$0 = \lambda p_1 \quad -(\lambda + \mu)\, p_2 + \mu p_3 \qquad\qquad (2.20)$$
$$- - - - - - - - - - - - - -$$
$$0 = \lambda p_{n-1} - (\lambda + \mu)\, p_n + \mu p_{n+1}$$
$$- - - - - - - - - - - -$$

From the first of these equations

$$\lambda p_0 = \mu p_1$$

i.e.
$$p_1 = p_0 \frac{\lambda}{\mu}.$$

Then from the second

$$\lambda p_0 - \mu p_1 - \lambda p_1 + \mu p_2 = 0$$
$$\therefore \quad \lambda p_1 = \mu p_2$$

so that
$$p_2 = p_1 \frac{\lambda}{\mu} = p_0 \left(\frac{\lambda}{\mu}\right)^2.$$

Proceeding in this way we obtain by successive substitution

$$p_n = p_0 \left(\frac{\lambda}{\mu}\right)^n. \qquad\qquad (2.21)$$

We have of course to satisfy the condition

$$\sum_{n=0}^{\infty} p_n = 1 \tag{2.22}$$

whence

$$p_0\left(1 + \frac{\lambda}{\mu} + \left(\frac{\lambda}{\mu}\right)^2 + \cdots\right) = 1$$

so that

$$p_0\left(\frac{1}{1 - \dfrac{\lambda}{\mu}}\right) = 1 \tag{2.23}$$

provided the geometric series in the brackets is convergent, i.e. $\lambda/\mu < 1$.

Thus provided $\lambda/\mu < 1$ (note it is a strict inequality) the steady-state solution is given by

$$p_0 = 1 - \frac{\lambda}{\mu} = 1 - \rho \tag{2.24}$$

$$p_n = \left(1 - \frac{\lambda}{\mu}\right)\left(\frac{\lambda}{\mu}\right)^n = (1 - \rho)\,\rho^n \tag{2.25}$$

where $\rho = \dfrac{\lambda}{\mu} < 1$.

Thus the number of customers in the system in the steady-state situation has a geometric distribution. When the system has run for a long time so that the steady-state solution has been achieved, p_n can be interpreted in one of two ways. It is the probability of finding n customers in the system at a particular instant or it is the long-run proportion of time that there are n customers in the system (as in Section 2.1).

Thus p_0 represents the proportion of time the system is empty so that:

$$\text{The proportion of time the server is idle} = p_0 = 1 - \rho, \tag{2.26}$$

$$\text{The proportion of time the server is busy} = 1 - p_0 = \rho. \tag{2.27}$$

The mean number in the system is found as the expected value of N.

$$E\{N\} = \sum_{n=0}^{\infty} np_n = (1 - \rho) \sum_{n=0}^{\infty} n\rho^n.$$

Now to sum the series $\sum_{n=0}^{\infty} n\rho^n$ we note that

$$f(\rho) = 1 + \rho + \rho^2 + \rho^3 + \cdots + \rho^n + \cdots = \frac{1}{1 - \rho}$$

$$\therefore \quad f'(\rho) = 1 + 2\rho + 3\rho^2 + \cdots + n\rho^{n-1} + \cdots = \frac{1}{(1 - \rho)^2}$$

$$\therefore \quad \rho f'(\rho) = \rho + 2\rho^2 + 3\rho^3 + \cdots + n\rho^n + \cdots = \frac{\rho}{(1 - \rho)^2}$$

$$\therefore \quad E\{N\} = \frac{\rho(1 - \rho)}{(1 - \rho)^2} = \frac{\rho}{1 - \rho}. \tag{2.28}$$

The mean number of customers in the system is

$$L = \frac{\rho}{1 - \rho} = \frac{\lambda}{\mu - \lambda}. \qquad (2.29)$$

The mean number of customers in the queue is similarly given as

$$Lq = \sum_{n=1}^{\infty} (n - 1) p_n \quad \text{[Note the lower summation limit]}$$

$$= \sum_{n=1}^{\infty} n p_n - \sum_{n=1}^{\infty} p_n$$

$$= \sum_{n=0}^{\infty} n p_n - (1 - p_0)$$

$$\therefore \quad Lq = L - \rho = \frac{\rho^2}{(1 - \rho)} = \frac{\lambda^2}{\mu(\mu - \lambda)}. \qquad (2.30)$$

We can also write equation (2.30) in the form

$$L = Lq + \rho. \qquad (2.31)$$

The quantity $\rho = \lambda/\mu$ is often referred to as the traffic intensity. It is the average number of customers to arrive in time $1/\mu$, the average service time. Provided it is strictly less than one a steady-state solution will be reached after a long time.

Example 1

Television sets for repair, arrive at random at an average rate of 4 per day to a single repairman who takes an average of $1\frac{1}{2}$ hours to carry out each repair, it being assumed that the repair times have a negative exponential distribution. What is the average number of television sets in the workshop? What is the probability that an arriving set will find at least 3 sets in front of it? The repairman works an eight hour day.

The arrival rate is 4 per eight hours i.e. $\frac{1}{2}$ per hour so that $\lambda = \frac{1}{2}$ (sets/hour). The mean repair time ($1/\mu$) is $\frac{3}{2}$ hours so that $\mu = \frac{2}{3}$ (repairs/hour).

Thus $\rho = \lambda/\mu = \frac{3}{4}$ is less than one so that a steady-state solution will exist.

The average number of sets in the workshop is the average number in the system which by equation (2.29) is

$$L = \frac{\rho}{1 - \rho} = 3.$$

We want to find the probability that there are three or more sets in the system at a given moment. This is

$$p_3 + p_4 + p_5 + \cdots = (1 - \rho) \rho^3 (1 + \rho + \rho^2 + \cdots) = \rho^3 = \tfrac{27}{64}.$$

Example 2

Lorries arrive at an average rate of 8 per day at an unloading bay which operates 24 hours a day. The time to unload a lorry averages 2 hours. It is assumed that inter-arrival times and unloading times have negative exponential distributions. Find the average number of lorries in the yard waiting to be unloaded but excluding the one at the bay. If this number exceeds 3 serious congestion problems can arise. Is this likely to happen?

In this case $\lambda = \frac{1}{3}$ lorry per hour and $\mu = \frac{1}{2}$ lorry per hour so that $\rho = \frac{2}{3}$. Thus the average number in the queue is

$$Lq = \frac{\rho^2}{(1 - \rho)} = \frac{4}{9} \cdot 3 = \frac{4}{3}.$$

The probability that there are 4 or more lorries in the system is $\rho^4 = \frac{16}{81}$. Thus there is about a 20% chance of such congestion occurring, or alternatively it will occur for about 20% of the time.

2.3   Waiting-Time Distributions

In this section we shall consider the time that a customer has to wait in the queue. This is defined to be the time that elapses between his arrival in the system and the moment his service commences. This is referred to as his queueing time. The time he spends in the system is the sum of his queueing time and his service time.

The queueing time is a random variable X which in general is a continuous variable which takes on positive values. However, for those customers who arrive to find an empty system, the queueing time is zero.

Thus

$$\Pr(X = 0) = p_0 = 1 - \rho = 1 - \frac{\lambda}{\mu}. \tag{2.32}$$

For $X > 0$, the queueing time will be a random variable with probability density function $\phi(x)$ where

$$\Pr(x \leqslant X \leqslant x + \delta x) = \phi(x) \, \delta x, \tag{2.33}$$

to first order in δx. But the event $(x \leqslant X \leqslant x + \delta x)$ is the union of the mutually exclusive events for $n = 1, 2, 3, \ldots$

the customer finds n other customers in the system on arrival, and
there are $(n - 1)$ service completions during time x, and
there is one service completion (of the customer immediately in front of him) in the interval $(x, x + \delta x)$.

For the particular case $n = 3$, in which our customer arrives at time t, the situation is illustrated in Fig. 2.4.

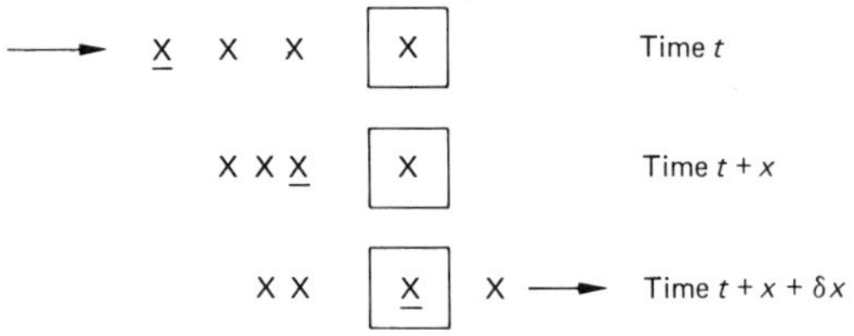

Fig. 2.4

Thus

$$\phi(x)\,\delta x = \sum_{n=1}^{\infty} p_n \cdot \frac{(\mu x)^{n-1}\,\mathrm{e}^{-\mu x}}{(n-1)!} \cdot \mu \delta x. \tag{2.34}$$

The three terms in the product that forms the summand are respectively the probability of n in the system on arrival, of $(n-1)$ services in time x (from equation (1.21); service is going on all of this time), and the probability of a service completion during $(x, x + \delta x)$.

Thus

$$\phi(x) = \mu \cdot \sum_{n=1}^{\infty} \left(\frac{\lambda}{\mu}\right)^{n} \left(1 - \frac{\lambda}{\mu}\right) \cdot \frac{(\mu x)^{n-1}\,\mathrm{e}^{-\mu x}}{(n-1)!}$$

$$= \left(1 - \frac{\lambda}{\mu}\right) \cdot \lambda\,\mathrm{e}^{-\mu x} \sum_{n=1}^{\infty} \frac{\left(\dfrac{\lambda}{\mu}\mu x\right)^{n-1}}{(n-1)!}$$

$$\therefore \quad \phi(x) = \frac{\lambda}{\mu}(\mu - \lambda)\,\mathrm{e}^{-(\mu - \lambda)x}; \quad x > 0. \tag{2.35}$$

since

$$\sum_{n=1}^{\infty} \frac{(\lambda x)^{n-1}}{(n-1)!} = \mathrm{e}^{\lambda x}.$$

We note that

$$\int_{0}^{\infty} \phi(x)\,\mathrm{d}x = \frac{\lambda}{\mu} \quad \text{and is not 1.}$$

However, if we add to this the probability that $X = 0$, so that we cover the entire range of values of the queueing time then

$$\Pr(X = 0) + \int_{0}^{\infty} \phi(x)\,\mathrm{d}x = 1.$$

The queueing time is a random variable that is part discrete, part continuous. There is a finite probability that it takes the value zero. For other values we treat it as a continuous random variable with probability density function $\phi(x)$ as given by equation (2.35).

The total time that a customer spends in the system is a random variable $Y = X + T$ where X is his queueing time and T is his service time, which will have a negative exponential distribution for the M/M/1 system. If Y has probability density function $\psi(y)$ and distribution function $\Psi(y)$ then

$$\Psi(y) = \Pr(Y \leqslant y) = \Pr(X = 0)\,\Pr(T \leqslant y) + \int_{0}^{y} \phi(x)\,\Pr(T \leqslant y - x)\,\mathrm{d}x.$$

But since T has a negative exponential distribution with mean $1/\mu$,

$$\Pr(T \leqslant y) = 1 - e^{-\mu y} \quad \text{(from equation (1.16))}.$$

$$\therefore \quad \Psi(y) = \left(1 - \frac{\lambda}{\mu}\right)(1 - e^{-\mu y}) + \int_0^y \frac{\lambda}{\mu}(\mu - \lambda)\, e^{-(\mu - \lambda)x}(1 - e^{-\mu(y - x)})\, dx$$

$$= \left(1 - \frac{\lambda}{\mu}\right)(1 - e^{-\mu y}) + \frac{\lambda}{\mu}(\mu - \lambda)\int_0^y e^{-(\mu - \lambda)x}\, dx$$

$$- \frac{\lambda}{\mu}(\mu - \lambda)\, e^{-\mu y}\int_0^y e^{\lambda x}\, dx$$

$$= \frac{\mu - \lambda}{\mu}(1 - e^{-\mu y}) + \frac{\lambda}{\mu}(1 - e^{-(\mu - \lambda)y}) - \frac{(\mu - \lambda)}{\mu}\, e^{-\mu y}(e^{\lambda y} - 1)$$

$$\therefore \quad \Psi(y) = 1 - e^{-(\mu - \lambda)y}; \quad y \geqslant 0. \tag{2.36}$$

On differentiation we obtain for the probability density function

$$\psi(y) = (\mu - \lambda)\, e^{-(\mu - \lambda)y}; \quad y \geqslant 0. \tag{2.37}$$

Thus the time in the system has a negative exponential distribution with parameter $(\mu - \lambda)$.

The average value for the queueing time is

$$W_q = E\{X\} = 0 \cdot \Pr(X = 0) + \int_0^\infty x\phi(x)\, dx$$

$$= \int_0^\infty \frac{\lambda(\mu - \lambda)}{\mu}\, x\, e^{-(\mu - \lambda)x}\, dx$$

$$= \frac{\lambda(\mu - \lambda)}{\mu} \cdot \frac{1}{(\mu - \lambda)^2}$$

$$\therefore \quad W_q = \frac{\lambda}{\mu(\mu - \lambda)}. \tag{2.38}$$

The average time spent in the system is

$$W = E\{Y\} = \int_0^\infty y\psi(y)\, dy = \frac{1}{(\mu - \lambda)}. \tag{2.39}$$

Of course

$$E\{Y\} = E\{X\} + E\{T\}$$

$$= \frac{\lambda}{\mu(\mu - \lambda)} + \frac{1}{\mu}$$

$$= \frac{1}{\mu - \lambda}$$

as before.

Example 1

Workmen in a factory shop are required, at the completion of stage 1 of a production process, to bring their work to a single inspector, who inspects and corrects (if necessary) their work before it proceeds to stage 2. Observations over a long period of time indicate that the men arrive at random at an average rate of 4 per hour. If it is assumed that the inspection time has a negative exponential distribution, at what rate must the inspector work if at least 80% of the men must spend less than 10 minutes away from productive work when they come to the inspector?

For this case if we choose our time units as minutes, $\lambda = 1/15$ and μ is to be found.

The time out of production is the time in the system, i.e. queueing time plus inspection (and correction) time and has density function

$$\psi(y) = (\mu - \lambda)\, e^{-(\mu - \lambda)y}, \quad y \geqslant 0$$

by equation (2.37).

We require to find μ so that

$$\int_0^{10} (\mu - \lambda)\, e^{-(\mu - \lambda)y}\, dy = 0.8,$$

i.e. the probability that the time in the system is less than 10 minutes is 0.8. This will give a lower bound for μ.

$$\therefore \quad [-e^{-(\mu - \lambda)y}]_0^{10} = 0.8$$

$$\therefore \quad 1 - e^{-(\mu - \lambda)10} = 0.8$$

$$\therefore \quad e^{-10(\mu - \lambda)} = 0.2$$

$$\therefore \quad 10(\mu - \lambda) = -\ln(0.2)$$

$$\therefore \quad \mu = \lambda - \frac{\ln(0.2)}{10}$$

$$= \tfrac{1}{15} - \tfrac{1}{10}\ln(0.2)$$

$$= 0.2276104 \text{ inspections/minute.}$$

Thus the mean inspection time $(1/\mu)$ must be less than 4.39 minutes.

2.4 Some Numerical Results

It is possible to calculate some of the simple properties of the M/M/1 queue as given by the formulae of the previous two sections. A simple BASIC program to do this and tabulate the results is given in this section.

It is assumed that $\mu = 1$ (i.e. the average service time has been made our unit of time) so that ρ [RHO in the table, RO in the program] is equal to λ, the average rate of arrivals. The headings in the table are self explanatory and the program is not difficult to understand. Line 90 merely formats all the numerical values output to be in fixed decimal notation (the 2 at the front) with 3 decimal places and each value occupying 9 characters. It is peculiar to the BBC microcomputer but other computers are likely to have an equivalent.

The tabulated values indicate what has been referred to before, viz. that low values of ρ will be good for the customers in terms of low numbers in the system and short queueing time, but mean that the service facility is idle for a large proportion of the time. It is also interesting to see that as ρ approaches 1, the mean number in the system (and the queue) and the mean time spent queueing increases very rapidly indeed. A very comprehensive set of tables and graphs dealing with a wide variety of queueing systems has recently been compiled by F. S. Hillier and O. S. Yu.

```
LIST
    10 PRINT "PROPERTIES OF THE M/M/1 QUEUE."
    20 PRINT"     RHO      MEAN NO. MEAN NO. AV. TIME AV. TIME PROP TIME"
    30 PRINT"              IN SYST   IN Q    IN SYST   IN Q    SRV IDLE"
    90 @%=&20309
   100 FOR R=2 TO 98 STEP 2
   110 RO=R/100
   120 L=RO/(1-RO)
   130 LQ=L-RO
   140 W=1/(1-RO)
   150 WQ=W-1
   160 P=1-RO
   170 PRINT RO,L,LQ,W,WQ,P
   180 NEXT R
   200 END
```

PROPERTIES OF THE M/M/1 QUEUE.

RHO	MEAN NO. IN SYST	MEAN NO. IN Q	AV. TIME IN SYST	AV. TIME IN Q	PROP TIME SRV IDLE
0.020	0.020	0.000	1.020	0.020	0.980
0.040	0.042	0.002	1.042	0.042	0.960
0.060	0.064	0.004	1.064	0.064	0.940
0.080	0.087	0.007	1.087	0.087	0.920
0.100	0.111	0.011	1.111	0.111	0.900
0.120	0.136	0.016	1.136	0.136	0.880
0.140	0.163	0.023	1.163	0.163	0.860
0.160	0.190	0.030	1.190	0.190	0.840
0.180	0.220	0.040	1.220	0.220	0.820
0.200	0.250	0.050	1.250	0.250	0.800
0.220	0.282	0.062	1.282	0.282	0.780
0.240	0.316	0.076	1.316	0.316	0.760
0.260	0.351	0.091	1.351	0.351	0.740
0.280	0.389	0.109	1.389	0.389	0.720
0.300	0.429	0.129	1.429	0.429	0.700
0.320	0.471	0.151	1.471	0.471	0.680
0.340	0.515	0.175	1.515	0.515	0.660
0.360	0.562	0.203	1.563	0.563	0.640
0.380	0.613	0.233	1.613	0.613	0.620
0.400	0.667	0.267	1.667	0.667	0.600
0.420	0.724	0.304	1.724	0.724	0.580
0.440	0.786	0.346	1.786	0.786	0.560
0.460	0.852	0.392	1.852	0.852	0.540
0.480	0.923	0.443	1.923	0.923	0.520
0.500	1.000	0.500	2.000	1.000	0.500
0.520	1.083	0.563	2.083	1.083	0.480
0.540	1.174	0.634	2.174	1.174	0.460
0.560	1.273	0.713	2.273	1.273	0.440
0.580	1.381	0.801	2.381	1.381	0.420
0.600	1.500	0.900	2.500	1.500	0.400
0.620	1.632	1.012	2.632	1.632	0.380
0.640	1.778	1.138	2.778	1.778	0.360
0.660	1.941	1.281	2.941	1.941	0.340
0.680	2.125	1.445	3.125	2.125	0.320
0.700	2.333	1.633	3.333	2.333	0.300
0.720	2.571	1.851	3.571	2.571	0.280
0.740	2.846	2.106	3.846	2.846	0.260
0.760	3.167	2.407	4.167	3.167	0.240
0.780	3.545	2.765	4.545	3.545	0.220
0.800	4.000	3.200	5.000	4.000	0.200
0.820	4.556	3.736	5.556	4.556	0.180
0.840	5.250	4.410	6.250	5.250	0.160
0.860	6.143	5.283	7.143	6.143	0.140
0.880	7.333	6.453	8.333	7.333	0.120
0.900	9.000	8.100	10.000	9.000	0.100
0.920	11.500	10.580	12.500	11.500	0.080
0.940	15.667	14.727	16.667	15.667	0.060
0.960	24.000	23.040	25.000	24.000	0.040
0.980	49.000	48.020	50.000	49.000	0.020

Exercises 2

1 Show that the solution of the equations

$$\frac{\mathrm{d}p_{\mathrm{R}}(t)}{\mathrm{d}t} = -\lambda p_{\mathrm{R}}(t) + \mu p_{\mathrm{S}}(t)$$

$$\frac{\mathrm{d}p_{\mathrm{S}}(t)}{\mathrm{d}t} = \lambda p_{\mathrm{R}}(t) - \mu p_{\mathrm{S}}(t)$$

where

$$p_{\mathrm{R}}(t) + p_{\mathrm{S}}(t) = 1,$$

with initial values $p_{\mathrm{R}}(0)$ and $p_{\mathrm{S}}(0)$ for the probabilities when $t = 0$, is

$$p_{\mathrm{R}}(t) = \frac{\mu}{\lambda + \mu}\left[1 - \mathrm{e}^{-(\lambda + \mu)t}\right] + p_{\mathrm{R}}(0)\,\mathrm{e}^{-(\lambda + \mu)t}$$

$$p_{\mathrm{S}}(t) = \frac{\lambda}{\lambda + \mu}\left[1 - \mathrm{e}^{-(\lambda + \mu)t}\right] + p_{\mathrm{S}}(0)\,\mathrm{e}^{-(\lambda + \mu)t}$$

2 An operative is in charge of a single machine which breaks down at random in running time at an average rate λ. The time taken by the operative to repair the machine and set it running again is a *constant c*. Let p_{R} denote the long-run proportion of time for which the machine is running. Consider a *long* period of time T. How many breakdowns will occur in this time and how long will they take to repair? Deduce that $p_{\mathrm{R}} = 1/(1 + \lambda c)$.

3 An operative is in charge of a single machine which is stopped for replenishment of raw material after every k minutes of running time. The time to replace the material takes c minutes and is constant. Show that the proportion of time for which the machine is actually running is

$$p_{\mathrm{R}} = 1 \bigg/ \left(1 + \frac{c}{k}\right)$$

4 The results contained in Section 2.1 and in Questions 2 and 3 show that we can obtain an expression for the proportion of time that the machine is running (a quantity of practical significance) of the form

$1/(1 + \text{Average breakdown rate} \times \text{Average repair time})$.

Verify that this is so and note that the result is true whether the stops occur at random or regularly in running time, or whether the repair time has a negative exponential distribution or is a constant.

Will this result be true for any pattern of breakdowns and any distribution of repair times? Can we interpret p_{R} as the probability that the machine is running at an arbitrary moment in time in the steady state?

5 Telephone calls to an operator arrive at random at an average rate λ. If she is busy when a call arrives then the call is lost. The time to deal with a call has a distribution with probability density function $\mu\mathrm{e}^{-\mu t}$; $t \geqslant 0$.

If initially the operator is busy with a call show that the probability that she is busy at time t wiii be a function $p(t)$ such that

$$p(t) = e^{-\mu t} + \lambda \int_0^t [1 - p(x)] e^{-\mu(t-x)} \, dx.$$

From this deduce a differential equation for $p(t)$ and hence obtain the function $p(t)$.

6 For the system of equations

$$0 = \qquad -\lambda p_0 + \mu p_1$$
$$0 = \lambda p_{n-1} - (\lambda + \mu) p_n + \mu p_{n+1} \quad \text{for } n \geq 1$$

where $\dfrac{\lambda}{\mu} < 1$, and $\sum\limits_{n=0}^{\infty} p_n = 1$, construct a full proof by induction that

$$p_n = \left(1 - \frac{\lambda}{\mu}\right)\left(\frac{\lambda}{\mu}\right)^n.$$

7 Consider the equations $\left(\dfrac{\lambda}{\mu} < 1\right)$

$$0 = \qquad -\lambda p_0 \qquad + \mu p_1$$
$$0 = \lambda p_0 - (\lambda + \mu) \, p_1 + \mu p_2$$
$$0 = \lambda p_1 - (\lambda + \mu) \, p_2 + \mu p_3$$
$$- - - - - - - - - - - -$$

$$\text{etc.}$$

where $p_n = \Pr(N = n)$.

If $P(z) = \sum\limits_{n=0}^{\infty} p_n z^n$, show by multiplying the successive equations by z^0, z^1, z^2 etc. that $P(z) = \dfrac{p_0}{1 - \rho z}$ where $\rho = \dfrac{\lambda}{\mu}$, and use the condition that $\sum\limits_{n=0}^{\infty} p_n = 1$ to show that $P(z) = \dfrac{(1 - \rho)}{1 - \rho z}$. Deduce the value of p_n.

8 Use the generating function $P(z)$ in Question 7 to show that (compare equation (2.28))

$$E\{N\} = \frac{\rho}{1 - \rho}; \quad \text{Var}\{N\} = \frac{\rho}{(1 - \rho)^2}.$$

9 Lorries arrive at a warehouse at random at an average rate of 1 every 50 minutes. The time to unload a lorry has an exponential distribution with a mean of 40 minutes. Find the proportion of time that the unloading bay is free and the mean number of lorries in the system.

10 Refer to Question 9. If new unloading equipment was installed at the bay the mean unloading time would be reduced to 30 minutes. The total cost of the new equipment would be £150 per week above present costs. If an idle lorry in the system costs £2 per hour and the system operates for 40 hours each week do you suggest that the new equipment is installed?

11 Barges arrive at a lock at an average rate of 4 per hour. The time to pass through the lock has a mean of 10 minutes. What is the mean time a barge has to wait before the lock is free? What is the probability that more than three barges are actually waiting? What assumptions have you made in answering this problem?

12 A simplified model of a telephone line is as follows. Calls are made on the line at random at average rate λ and the length of the call is exponentially distributed with mean $1/\mu$. If callers find the line engaged they immediately abandon the call.

Set up a pair of differential equations to enable you to find the probability $p_E(t)$ that the line is engaged at time t. Find $p_E(t)$ if the line is engaged at time zero.

13 Customers to a single-server queue arrive at random at an average rate of 6 per hour. Customers to a second single-server queue arrive at random at an average rate of 4 per hour. In both queues service has a negative exponential distribution with mean 5 minutes.

Find the average number of customers in each system, the average number in each queue and the average queueing time of a customer in each queue.

If one of the servers falls sick and one server has to cope with all the customers recalculate the average number in the system, in the queue and the average queueing time.

14 Show that for the M/M/1 queue with the notation of Sections 2.2 and 2.3
$$L = \lambda W, \quad L_q = \lambda W_q.$$

15 For the M/M/1 queue with the notation of Sections 2.2 and 2.3 find:
(a) the expected number in the system given that the system is not empty;
(b) the expected queueing time of customers who have to queue;
(c) the average length of non-empty queues.

16 Customers arrive at random at a check-out at an average rate of 12 per hour. Service time has an exponential distribution at an average rate μ. If the *queueing* time of at least 90% of the customers should be less than 4 minutes, show that μ must exceed μ_0 where
$$\mu_0 \, e^{4\mu_0} = 2 \, e^{\frac{4}{5}}.$$

17 Cars arrive at a toll bridge at random at an average rate of 90 per hour. The average time taken to pass through the toll booth is 36 seconds. There have been many complaints concerning the delay and congestion. The authority which runs the bridge is prepared to introduce an automatic device which should reduce the average time to pass through the toll booth to 30 seconds, but the authority will only introduce this device if certain criteria are satisfied. These are that under the old system the average number of cars queueing exceeds 5 and under the new system the automatic device will be in use at least 30% of the time.

Are the criteria likely to be met? State the assumptions you have made.

18 Customers to an M/M/1 queue arrive at an average rate λ. The cost of providing service at rate μ is £$S\mu$ per unit time and the cost of keeping a customer in the system is £C per unit time. S and C are known constants. Given λ what is the optimum value of μ on the basis of minimising the total cost per unit time of running the system?

19   Consider the derivation of the queueing time density function

$$\phi(x) = \frac{\lambda}{\mu}(\mu - \lambda)\, e^{-(\mu - \lambda)x}; \quad x \geqslant 0. \tag{2.35}$$

Let the queueing time density of a customer who finds r customers in the system $(r \geqslant 1)$ be $\phi_r(x)$. The queueing time of such a customer will consist of the sum of r independent service times each of which have a negative exponential distribution with mean $1/\mu$. (The residual service time of the customer being served also has this distribution.) Use equation (1.12) to deduce that $\phi_r(x)$ has Laplace Transform

$$\left(\frac{\mu}{\mu + s}\right)^r.$$

[See also Exercises 1, Question 3.]

Hence show that $\phi(x)$ has Laplace Transform

$$\Phi^*(s) = \sum_{r=1}^{\infty} p_r \left(\frac{\mu}{\mu + s}\right)^r$$

$$= \left(1 - \frac{\lambda}{\mu}\right) \sum_{r=1}^{\infty} \left(\frac{\lambda}{\mu + s}\right)^r = \frac{\lambda}{\mu} \cdot \frac{\mu - \lambda}{\mu - \lambda + s},$$

and so find $\phi(x)$.

20   Programs arrive to a mainframe computer at random at an average rate of 18 per minute. The time to process a program has a negative exponential distribution with an average time of 3 seconds. It has been suggested that the programs could be equally divided into two independent arriving streams each of which, using a cheaper minicomputer also operating exponentially, would be processed at half the rate of the mainframe. Would the programs experience smaller average queueing time and time spent in the system by using the two minis rather than the mainframe? What would happen if n minis each working at $(1/n)$th of the rate of the mainframe were used?

3
Birth–Death Models

3.1 The Birth–Death Equations

We can extend the formulation of the M/M/1 queue as given in Section 2.2 to deal with the situation where the arrival rate and the service completion rate is a function of n, the number of customers in the system.

Thus we consider the case where arrivals occur at random but at rate λ_n when there are n in the system. Similarly service times have a negative exponential distribution but this has mean $1/\mu_n$ when there are n customers in the system. As before we let the number in the system at time t be the random variable $N(t)$ and denote the probability that $N(t)$ takes on the value n $(=0, 1, 2, \ldots)$ by $p_n(t)$;

$$\Pr(N(t) = n) = p_n(t). \tag{3.1}$$

The arguments used in Section 2.2 can then be used to derive the equations (to first order in δt):

$$
\left.
\begin{aligned}
&p_0(t + \delta t) = p_0(t)(1 - \lambda_0\,\delta t) + p_1(t)(1 - \lambda_1\,\delta t)\,\mu_1\,\delta t \\[4pt]
&p_1(t + \delta t) = p_0(t)\,\lambda_0\,\delta t + p_1(t)(1 - \lambda_1\,\delta t)(1 - \mu_1\,\delta t) + p_2(t)(1 - \lambda_2\,\delta t)\,\mu_2\,\delta t \\[4pt]
&\qquad - - - - - - - - \\[4pt]
&\text{and for } n \geqslant 2 \\[4pt]
&p_n(t + \delta t) = p_{n-1}(t)\,\lambda_{n-1}\,\delta t(1 - \mu_{n-1}\,\delta t) + p_n(t)(1 - \lambda_n\,\delta t)(1 - \mu_n\,\delta t) \\[4pt]
&\qquad\qquad + p_{n+1}(t)(1 - \lambda_{n+1}\,\delta t)\,\mu_{n+1}\,\delta t
\end{aligned}
\right\} \tag{3.2}
$$

The only modification to the argument used in deriving equations (2.16) to (2.18) is to note that the arrival and service rates for the interval $(t, t + \delta t)$ have to be in line with the number in the system at time t.

Straightforward manipulation of equations (3.2) yields the following set of differential equations for the $p_n(t)$:

$$
\left.
\begin{aligned}
&\frac{dp_0(t)}{dt} = \qquad\quad -\,\lambda_0\,p_0(t) \quad + \quad \mu_1\,p_1(t) \\[6pt]
&\frac{dp_1(t)}{dt} = \lambda_0\,p_0(t) - (\lambda_1 + \mu_1)\,p_1(t) + \mu_2\,p_2(t) \\[6pt]
&\qquad - - - - - - - - \\[6pt]
&\frac{dp_n(t)}{dt} = \lambda_{n-1}\,p_{n-1}(t) - (\lambda_n + \mu_n)\,p_n(t) + \mu_{n+1}\,p_{n+1}(t) \\[6pt]
&\qquad - - - - - - - -
\end{aligned}
\right\} \tag{3.3}
$$

These equations are often referred to as the birth–death equations and have found applications in the modelling of population growth. The 'arrival' of a customer corresponds to a birth and service completion has more sinister overtones. We shall see that these equations can be valuable in modelling a range of queueing situations.

To date no time-dependent solution of the equations (3.3) has been obtained in general, although a few special cases have been solved. The conditions for the existence of a steady-state solution have been investigated by Karlin and McGregor and Reuter [see the references for Chapter 2], and we state without proof that equations (3.3) will have a steady-state solution, $\lim_{t \to \infty} p_n(t) = p_n$ provided the series

$$1 + \frac{\lambda_0}{\mu_1} + \frac{\lambda_0 \lambda_1}{\mu_1 \mu_2} + \frac{\lambda_0 \lambda_1 \lambda_2}{\mu_1 \mu_2 \mu_3} + \dots \text{ is convergent.} \tag{3.4}$$

Our standard technique of realising that in the steady state limit $\lim_{t \to \infty} \dfrac{\mathrm{d}p_n(t)}{\mathrm{d}t} = 0$, allows the equations for the p_n to be written down and solved. Thus we obtain

$$\left.\begin{aligned}
0 &= \qquad\quad -\lambda_0 p_0 + \qquad\quad \mu_1 p_1 \\
0 &= \lambda_0 p_0 - (\lambda_1 + \mu_1) p_1 + \mu_2 p_2 \\
0 &= \lambda_1 p_1 - (\lambda_2 + \mu_2) p_2 + \mu_3 p_3 \\
0 &= \lambda_{n-1} p_{n-1} - (\lambda_n + \mu_n) p_n + \mu_{n+1} p_{n+1}
\end{aligned}\right\} \tag{3.5}$$

$$\text{etc.}$$

From the first of these equations

$$\lambda_0 p_0 = \mu_1 p_1$$

whence

$$p_1 = p_0 \frac{\lambda_0}{\mu_1}.$$

Then from the second

$$\lambda_1 p_1 = \mu_2 p_2$$

whence

$$p_2 = \frac{\lambda_1}{\mu_2} p_1 = \frac{\lambda_0 \lambda_1}{\mu_1 \mu_2} p_0.$$

We can proceed in this way and readily obtain (the reader is urged to write out a full induction proof)

$$p_n = \frac{\lambda_0 \lambda_1 \lambda_2 \dots \lambda_{n-1}}{\mu_1 \mu_2 \mu_3 \dots \mu_n} p_0. \tag{3.6}$$

To find p_0 we have to use the condition

$$\sum_{n=0}^{\infty} p_n = 1 \tag{3.7}$$

whence

$$p_0 = 1/S, \tag{3.8}$$

where

$$S = 1 + \frac{\lambda_0}{\mu_1} + \frac{\lambda_0 \lambda_1}{\mu_1 \mu_2} + \cdots = \sum_{n=0}^{\infty} \frac{\lambda_0 \lambda_1 \ldots \lambda_{n-1}}{\mu_1 \mu_2 \ldots \mu_n}. \tag{3.9}$$

Thus we can understand the necessity (though not the sufficiency) of the requirement that S be convergent in order for a steady-state solution to exist. We shall see in the next section that we can model a number of queueing situations with the equations (3.3) and investigate their steady-state solution with equations (3.6) and (3.8).

3.2 Models Using the Birth–Death Equations

A   A queue with limited waiting room

Consider a single-server queue with random arrivals at rate λ, and negative exponential service at rate μ but in which there is only room for N customers. It is assumed that when the system is full, i.e. contains N customers then new arrivals go elsewhere.

We can model this along the lines of Section 3.1 with

$$\lambda_0 = \lambda_1 = \lambda_2 \ldots \lambda_{N-1} = \lambda$$

$$\lambda_N = \lambda_{N+1} = \ldots \quad\quad = 0$$

$$\mu_1 = \mu_2 = \mu_3 \ldots \quad\quad = \mu_N = \mu.$$

Thus with $\rho = \dfrac{\lambda}{\mu}$, equation (3.6) gives

$$p_n = p_0 \, \rho^n \quad \text{for } n = 0, 1, 2, \ldots, N$$

$$p_n = 0 \quad\quad \text{for } n > N.$$

Condition (3.7) becomes

$$p_0 \sum_{n=0}^{N} \rho^n = 1$$

and $S = \displaystyle\sum_{n=0}^{N} \rho^n$ is certainly convergent (it is a finite series!).

Thus

$$p_0 = \frac{1-\rho}{1-\rho^{N+1}}, \tag{3.10}$$

$$p_n = \frac{(1-\rho)\,\rho^n}{1-\rho^{N+1}}. \tag{3.11}$$

$p_N = \dfrac{(1-\rho)\,\rho^N}{1-\rho^{N+1}}$ has an interesting interpretation for this problem. It is the proportion of time that the system is full and so is the proportion of potential customers who are lost and go elsewhere for service.

B   A queue in which customers are discouraged

It is easy to envisage that customers will be discouraged from joining the queue if on arrival they find a large number of customers in the system already. This can be modelled by making λ_n a suitably decreasing function of n.

Consider a single-server queue with exponential service at rate μ and random arrivals at rate λ, but in which only a proportion $1/(n+1)$ of arrivals actually join the system when there are n customers in the system.

In this case we have $\mu_n = \mu$ for all n and $\lambda_n = \dfrac{\lambda}{n+1}$. This is a special case of the more general model, $\lambda_n = \lambda f(n)$ where $f(n)$ is a decreasing function of n. Of course it might be very difficult to find a form for $f(n)$ which truly mirrors customer behaviour and our example is a relatively crude attempt to do this.

For this model we obtain

$$p_1 = \frac{\lambda}{\mu} p_0, \quad p_2 = \frac{\lambda \cdot \lambda}{\mu \cdot 2\mu} p_0, \quad p_3 = \frac{\lambda \cdot \lambda \cdot \lambda}{\mu \cdot 2\mu \cdot 3\mu} p_0 \text{ etc.}$$

and in general

$$p_n = p_0 \cdot \left(\frac{\lambda}{\mu}\right)^n \cdot \frac{1}{n!} = \frac{\rho^n}{n!} p_0$$

where $\rho = \dfrac{\lambda}{\mu}$.

Since we require $\sum\limits_{n=0}^{\infty} p_n = 1$ we obtain

$$p_0 \sum_{n=0}^{\infty} \frac{\rho^n}{n!} = 1 \quad \text{i.e. } p_0 \, e^\rho = 1$$

so that

$$p_0 = e^{-\rho}.$$

There is no problem with the convergence of S as defined by equation (3.9). The exponential series is convergent for all values of ρ.

Thus

$$p_n = \frac{\rho^n e^{-\rho}}{n!}. \tag{3.12}$$

Thus we see that the number in the system in the steady state has a Poisson distribution with mean ρ and variance ρ.

C   A self-service system

If we assume random arrivals at rate λ and assume that customers serve themselves exponentially at rate μ, then we can model this with

$$\lambda_n = \lambda; \quad \mu_n = n\mu \quad \text{for all } n.$$

Then as in B it is easy to show that

$$p_n = \frac{\rho^n}{n!} p_0 \quad \text{where } \rho = \frac{\lambda}{\mu}.$$

Thus again $p_n = \frac{\rho^n e^{-\rho}}{n!}$ as in the previous example.

3.3 A Queue with Two Servers

In this section we consider the M/M/2 system in which customers arrive at random at rate λ and are served by one of two servers, each having service time that has a negative exponential distribution with mean $1/\mu$. We can envisage the system set up as in Fig. 3.1. Customers form a central queue (if both servers are busy on arrival) and then go to the first server to become available. Alternatively they could form two separate queues in front of the two servers but are free to go to the first server to become free, and do this in the order of their arrival. Of course this does not always happen in the real world. If we join the 'wrong queue', and find that a customer in front of us has a particularly long service, then we might still be waiting when those who arrived after us have been served by the other server; a frustrating experience and our system avoids it.

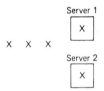

Fig. 3.1

We can model the problem above in terms of the birth–death equations, and obtain the steady-state solution by putting

$$\lambda_n = \lambda \quad \text{for all } n \geqslant 0,$$

$$\mu_1 = \mu, \quad \mu_2 = 2\mu \quad \text{and indeed } \mu_n = 2\mu \quad \text{for } n \geqslant 2.$$

The steady-state probabilities are given by

$$p_1 = p_0 \frac{\lambda}{\mu}, \quad p_2 = p_0 \frac{\lambda^2}{2\mu^2}, \quad p_3 = p_0 \frac{\lambda^3}{2^2 \mu^3}, \quad p_4 = p_0 \frac{\lambda^4}{2^3 \mu^4} \ldots \text{etc.};$$

i.e.

$$p_n = 2 \left(\frac{\rho}{2} \right)^n p_0; \quad n \geqslant 1, \quad \text{where } \rho = \frac{\lambda}{\mu}. \tag{3.13}$$

Since $\sum_{n=0}^{\infty} p_n = 1,$

$$p_0 \left\{ 1 + 2 \left[\frac{\rho}{2} + \left(\frac{\rho}{2} \right)^2 + \cdots \right] \right\} = 1$$

$$\therefore \quad p_0 \left\{ 1 + \frac{\rho}{1 - \frac{\rho}{2}} \right\} = 1, \quad \text{provided } \left| \frac{\rho}{2} \right| < 1$$

so that
$$\Pr(N = 0) = p_0 = \frac{2 - \rho}{2 + \rho}, \tag{3.14}$$

and
$$\Pr(N = n) = p_n = 2 \left(\frac{2 - \rho}{2 + \rho} \right) \left(\frac{\rho}{2} \right)^n \quad \text{for } n \geqslant 1. \tag{3.15}$$

Note that in order for a steady-state solution to exist in the M/M/2 queue we must have $\rho < 2$, i.e. $\lambda < 2\mu$, as we might expect intuitively.

$$E\{N\} = \sum_{n=0}^{\infty} n p_n = \sum_{n=1}^{\infty} n p_n$$

$$= 2 \left(\frac{2 - \rho}{2 + \rho} \right) \sum_{n=1}^{\infty} n \left(\frac{\rho}{2} \right)^n$$

$$= 2 \left(\frac{2 - \rho}{2 + \rho} \right) \frac{\frac{\rho}{2}}{\left(1 - \frac{\rho}{2} \right)^2}$$

$$\therefore \quad E\{N\} = L = \frac{4\rho}{(2 + \rho)(2 - \rho)} = \frac{4\rho}{4 - \rho^2}. \tag{3.16}$$

For the expected number in the queue

$$L_q = \sum_{n=2}^{\infty} (n - 2) p_n = p_3 + 2 p_4 + 3 p_5 + \cdots$$

$$= \frac{2(2 - \rho)}{2 + \rho} \left\{ \left(\frac{\rho}{2} \right)^3 + 2 \left(\frac{\rho}{2} \right)^4 + 3 \left(\frac{\rho}{2} \right)^5 + \cdots \right\}$$

$$= 2 \left(\frac{2 - \rho}{2 + \rho} \right) \left(\frac{\rho}{2} \right)^2 \left\{ \left(\frac{\rho}{2} \right) + 2 \left(\frac{\rho}{2} \right)^2 + 3 \left(\frac{\rho}{2} \right)^3 + \cdots \right\}$$

$$= 2 \left(\frac{2 - \rho}{2 + \rho} \right) \left(\frac{\rho}{2} \right)^2 \left\{ \frac{\frac{\rho}{2}}{\left(1 - \frac{\rho}{2} \right)^2} \right\}$$

$$\therefore \quad L_q = \frac{\rho^3}{4 - \rho^2} = \frac{4\rho}{4 - \rho^2} - \rho. \tag{3.17}$$

We note from equation (3.16) that in the M/M/2 system

$$L = L_q + \rho \tag{3.18}$$

as was the case in the M/M/1 system.

We can derive the distribution of the queueing time X of an arbitrary customer, when the system is in the steady state, by an argument similar to that of Section 2.3.

When X is positive it will be a random variable with probability density function $\phi_2(x)$.

$$\Pr(x \leqslant X \leqslant x + \delta x) = \phi_2(x)\,\delta x.$$

But the probability on the left is the sum of the products for $n = 2, 3, 4, \ldots$

$\Pr(n$ in the system on arrival$) \times \Pr(n - 2$ services in $x)$
$$\times \Pr(\text{service completion in } (x, x + \delta x)).$$

Now $\Pr(n$ in the system on arrival$) = p_n$ as given by equation (3.15);

$$\Pr(n - 2 \text{ services in } x) = \frac{(2\mu x)^{n-2}\,e^{-2\mu x}}{(n-2)!}; \quad \text{(the rate of service is } 2\mu\text{)};$$

$$\Pr(\text{service completion in } (x, x + \delta x)) = 2\mu\delta x.$$

Thus

$$\phi_2(x) = \sum_{n=2}^{\infty} 2\left(\frac{2-\rho}{2+\rho}\right)\left(\frac{\rho}{2}\right)^n \cdot \frac{(2\mu x)^{n-2}\,e^{-2\mu x}}{(n-2)!} \cdot 2\mu; \quad x > 0.$$

$$\therefore \quad \phi_2(x) = 2\left(\frac{2-\rho}{2+\rho}\right) 2\mu\left(\frac{\lambda}{2\mu}\right)^2 e^{-2\mu x} \sum_{n=2}^{\infty} \frac{(\lambda x)^{n-2}}{(n-2)!}$$

$$\therefore \quad \phi_2(x) = \mu\left(\frac{2-\rho}{2+\rho}\right)\rho^2\,e^{-(2\mu-\lambda)x}; \quad x > 0. \tag{3.19}$$

Of course

$$\int_0^{\infty} \phi_2(x)\,dx \neq 1$$

and in order to obtain the complete distribution of X we have

$$\Pr(X = 0) = p_0 + p_1. \tag{3.20}$$

For the expected value of X

$$W_q = E\{X\} = \int_0^{\infty} x\phi_2(x)\,dx$$

$$= \frac{1}{\lambda}\frac{\rho^3}{4-\rho^2} \tag{3.21}$$

after a little algebra.

Notice that

$$L_q - \lambda W_q. \tag{3.22}$$

If L is the mean number in the system and W is the mean time in the system then

$$L = \lambda W. \tag{3.23}$$

This is readily verified since $W = W_q + \dfrac{1}{\mu}$. Also we have seen, in equation (3.18), that

$$L = L_q + \frac{\lambda}{\mu}.$$

Example 1

Customers to a single-server queue arrive at random at an average rate of 6 per hour. Customers to a second queue arrive at random at an average rate of 4 per hour. In both cases service has a negative exponential distribution with mean 5 minutes. Find the average number in the system in each case and the proportion of time each server is idle.

If the system is reorganised so that each server can deal with any of the customers, who now arrive at a two-server system, find the average number of customers in this system and the proportion of time each server is idle.

For the first queue, $\lambda = \frac{1}{10}$ customer/minute and $\mu = \frac{1}{5}$ service/minute, i.e. $\rho_1 = \frac{1}{2}$

$$\therefore \quad L_1 = \frac{\rho_1}{1 - \rho_1} = 1 \text{ and the proportion of time the first server is idle is } 1 - \rho_1 = \frac{1}{2}.$$

For the second queue, $\lambda = \frac{1}{15}$ customer/minute and $\mu = \frac{1}{5}$ service/minute, i.e. $\rho_2 = \frac{1}{3}$

$$\therefore \quad L_2 = \frac{1}{2} \text{ and the proportion of time the second server is idle} = \frac{2}{3}.$$

Thus with two separate queues the average number of customers in the system is $L_1 + L_2 = \frac{3}{2}$, and the proportion of idle time (on average) per server is $\frac{1}{2}(\frac{1}{2} + \frac{2}{3}) = \frac{7}{12}$.

For the combined system, customers arrive at random at an average rate of 10 per hour. Thus $\lambda = \frac{1}{6}, \mu = \frac{1}{5}$ and $\rho = \frac{5}{6}$. Thus by equation (3.16), $L = \frac{4\rho}{4 - \rho^2} = \frac{120}{119}$. This of course is considerably less than $L_1 + L_2 = \frac{3}{2}$.

$$p_0 = \frac{2 - \rho}{2 + \rho} = \frac{7}{17} \quad \text{and} \quad p_1 = 2p_0 \frac{\rho}{2} = \frac{35}{102}.$$

Each server is idle for a proportion $p_0 + \frac{1}{2}p_1$ of the time. This is based on the assumption that when there is just one customer in the system he is just as likely to be served by one server as the other. This quantity works out to be

$$\frac{7}{17} + \frac{35}{204} = \frac{119}{204} = \frac{7}{12} \text{ as before.}$$

Thus we see the advantage of merging two single-server queues into a two-server queue. The servers have no more work to do on average (there are no extra customers to serve), but we do avoid the situation where customers are *queueing* in front of one server while the other is idle. This reduces the number in the system on average.

3.4 The M/M/k Queue

It is possible to generalise the results of the previous section to a system with random arrivals at average rate λ, and k servers, each providing negative exponential service at rate μ.

The steady-state solution of the birth–death equations with

$$\lambda_1 = \lambda_2 = \lambda_n = \lambda \quad \text{for all } n,$$

and
$$\mu_1 = \mu, \quad \mu_2 = 2\mu, \quad \mu_3 = 3\mu, \ldots, \mu_k = k\mu,$$
$$\mu_n = k\mu \quad \text{for } n > k,$$

exists, provided
$$\frac{\lambda}{k\mu} < 1, \quad \text{i.e. } \lambda < k\mu.$$

The steady-state probabilities are given by

$$p_n = p_0 \cdot \frac{1}{n!} \left(\frac{\lambda}{\mu} \right)^n; \quad n = 0, 1, 2, \ldots, k-1 \qquad (3.24)$$

$$p_n = p_0 \cdot \frac{1}{k! \, k^{n-k}} \left(\frac{\lambda}{\mu} \right)^n; \quad n \geqslant k. \qquad (3.25)$$

p_0 can be evaluated using the condition $\sum\limits_{n=0}^{\infty} p_n = 1$.

The algebra is a bit more messy than in the previous case and we obtain (the reader should take the trouble to verify this result)

$$p_0 = \frac{1}{\left[\sum\limits_{n=0}^{k-1} \frac{1}{n!} \left(\frac{\lambda}{\mu} \right)^n \right] + \frac{1}{k!} \left(\frac{\lambda}{\mu} \right)^k \frac{k\mu}{k\mu - \lambda}}. \qquad (3.26)$$

N.B. It is not possible to obtain a closed form for the expression in square brackets in the denominator of equation (3.26). It is convenient to derive expressions for the average number in the system etc. in terms of p_0.

The probability that all k servers are busy at a particular time (this is also the probability that an arriving customer has to queue) is given by

$$\Pr(N \geqslant k) = \sum\limits_{n=k}^{\infty} p_n$$

$$= \frac{p_0}{(k-1)!} \left(\frac{\lambda}{\mu} \right)^{k-1} \left[\frac{\lambda}{k\mu} + \left(\frac{\lambda}{k\mu} \right)^2 + \cdots \right]$$

$$= \frac{\lambda \left(\frac{\lambda}{\mu} \right)^{k-1}}{(k-1)! \, (k\mu - \lambda)} p_0. \qquad (3.27)$$

The average number of customers in the queue is

$$L_q = \sum\limits_{n=k}^{\infty} (n-k) p_n$$

$$= \frac{p_0}{k!} \left(\frac{\lambda}{\mu} \right)^k \left[\frac{\lambda}{k\mu} + 2 \left(\frac{\lambda}{k\mu} \right)^2 + 3 \left(\frac{\lambda}{k\mu} \right)^3 + \cdots \right]$$

$$= \frac{p_0}{k!} \left(\frac{\lambda}{\mu} \right)^k \cdot \frac{\frac{\lambda}{k\mu}}{\left(1 - \frac{\lambda}{k\mu} \right)^2}$$

$$= \frac{\lambda\mu \left(\frac{\lambda}{\mu} \right)^k}{(k-1)! \, (k\mu - \lambda)^2} p_0. \qquad (3.28)$$

The average number of customers in the system is

$$L = \sum_{n=0}^{\infty} n p_n = \sum_{n=1}^{k-1} n p_n + \sum_{n=k}^{\infty} n p_n$$

$$= \sum_{n=1}^{k-1} n p_n + k \sum_{n=k}^{\infty} p_n + \sum_{n=k}^{\infty} (n-k) p_n$$

$$= \sum_{n=1}^{k-1} n p_n + k \sum_{n=k}^{\infty} p_n + L_q$$

$$= p_0 \frac{\lambda}{\mu} \left[1 + \frac{2}{2!} \frac{\lambda}{\mu} + \frac{3}{3!} \left(\frac{\lambda}{\mu} \right)^2 + \cdots \frac{(k-1)}{(k-1)!} \left(\frac{\lambda}{\mu} \right)^{k-2} \right]$$

$$+ \frac{k\mu \left(\dfrac{\lambda}{\mu} \right)^k}{(k-1)!\,(k\mu - \lambda)} p_0 + L_q$$

$$= \frac{\lambda}{\mu} p_0 \sum_{n=0}^{k-2} \frac{1}{n!} \left(\frac{\lambda}{\mu} \right)^n + \frac{k\mu \left(\dfrac{\lambda}{\mu} \right)^k}{(k-1)!\,(k\mu - \lambda)} p_0 + L_q$$

$$= \frac{\lambda}{\mu} p_0 \sum_{n=0}^{k-1} \frac{1}{n!} \left(\frac{\lambda}{\mu} \right)^n + \frac{k\mu \left(\dfrac{\lambda}{\mu} \right)^k p_0}{(k-1)!\,(k\mu - \lambda)} - \frac{\lambda}{\mu} p_0 \frac{\left(\dfrac{\lambda}{\mu} \right)^{k-1}}{(k-1)!} + L_q$$

$$\therefore \quad L = L_q + \frac{\lambda}{\mu} p_0 \left[\sum_{n=0}^{k-1} \frac{1}{n!} \left(\frac{\lambda}{\mu} \right)^n + \left(\frac{\lambda}{\mu} \right)^{k-1} \frac{(k\mu - k\mu + \lambda)}{(k-1)!\,(k\mu - \lambda)} \right]$$

$$\therefore \quad L = L_q + \frac{\lambda}{\mu} p_0 \left[\sum_{n=0}^{k-1} \frac{1}{n!} \left(\frac{\lambda}{\mu} \right)^n + \frac{1}{k!} \left(\frac{\lambda}{\mu} \right)^k \frac{k\mu}{k\mu - \lambda} \right]$$

$$\therefore \quad L = L_q + \frac{\lambda}{\mu} \tag{3.29}$$

on using equation (3.26).

For the queueing time of an arbitrary customer we repeat the argument of Sections 2.3 and 3.3.

$$\Pr(X = 0) = p_0 + p_1 + p_2 + \cdots + p_{k-1} = 1 - \Pr(N \geqslant k). \tag{3.30}$$

When $X > 0$ it has probability density function

$$\phi_k(x) = \frac{\mu p_0}{(k-1)!} \left(\frac{\lambda}{\mu} \right)^k e^{-(k\mu - \lambda)x}; \quad x > 0. \tag{3.31}$$

The mean queueing time is

$$W_q = \frac{\mu \left(\dfrac{\lambda}{\mu} \right)^k}{(k-1)!\,(k\mu - \lambda)^2} p_0. \tag{3.32}$$

The mean time spent in the system is obtained by adding to this the mean service time

$$\therefore \quad W = W_q + \frac{1}{\mu}. \tag{3.33}$$

Note that
$$L_q = \lambda W_q \tag{3.34}$$

and from equations (3.29) and (3.33)

$$L = \lambda W \tag{3.35}$$

so that these relationships generalise to the M/M/k system.

Example 1

Workmen in a factory have to bring their work to a quality control inspector before the work can proceed to the final stage of production. There are a large number of men and the arrival pattern is approximately random at an average rate of 20 per hour. The time to inspect a piece of work has a negative exponential distribution with mean 4 minutes. Find the average number of men in the system (i.e. away from their productive work) on the basis of (a) 1, (b) 2 and (c) 3 inspectors.

Let £C denote the hourly pay for an inspector and £D the hourly loss from having a workman idle. For what values of D and C is it worth employing 3 inspectors rather than 2?

(a) $\lambda = \dfrac{1}{3}$ customer/minute, $\mu = \dfrac{1}{4}$ inspection/minute

Thus $\dfrac{\lambda}{\mu} = \dfrac{4}{3} > 1$ and there is no steady-state solution with one inspector. The number in the system will just increase. This is not a reasonable way to run the system.

(b)   With $k = 2$ we have, from equation (3.26)

$$\frac{1}{p_0} = 1 + \frac{4}{3} + \frac{1}{2}\left(\frac{4}{3}\right)^2 \frac{2 \cdot \dfrac{1}{4}}{2 \cdot \dfrac{1}{4} - \dfrac{1}{3}}$$

$$= 1 + \frac{4}{3} + \frac{8}{9}\frac{\dfrac{1}{2}}{\dfrac{1}{6}} = 1 + \frac{4}{3} + \frac{8}{3} = \frac{15}{3}.$$

$$\therefore \quad p_0 = \frac{1}{5}.$$

We get the same result from equation (3.14) of course.
Then from equations (3.29) and (3.28)

$$L = \frac{4}{3} + \frac{\dfrac{1}{12} \cdot \left(\dfrac{4}{3}\right)^2}{\left(\dfrac{1}{6}\right)^2} \cdot \frac{1}{5} = \frac{4}{3} + \frac{16}{15}.$$

(c)   With $k = 3$ we obtain from equation (3.26)

$$\frac{1}{p_0} = 1 + \frac{4}{3} + \frac{1}{2!}\left(\frac{4}{3}\right)^2 + \frac{1}{3!}\left(\frac{4}{3}\right)^3 \cdot \frac{\frac{3}{4}}{\frac{3}{4} - \frac{1}{3}} = \frac{177}{45};$$

and from equations (3.29) and (3.28)

$$L = \frac{4}{3} + \frac{\frac{1}{12}\left(\frac{4}{3}\right)^3}{2!\left(\frac{5}{12}\right)^2} \cdot \frac{45}{177} = \frac{4}{3} + \frac{128}{5 \times 177}.$$

The cost per hour of employing the extra inspector is £C. This results in reducing the average number of idle workers by $\frac{16}{15} - \frac{128}{5 \times 177} = \frac{816}{885} \simeq 0.922$.

Thus provided $C < 0.922D$ the extra inspector generates an overall saving.

A simple BASIC program is given which calculates p_0, L, L_q, W, W_q as given by the formulae of this section for various values of λ/μ (RHO in table, R in program) and k. As written it covers the range of values for $k = 1, 4$ but this could clearly be extended. It is assumed that $\mu = 1$ so that time is measured in units of the mean service time. The reader is urged to check the logic of the program. The sum in square backets in equation (3.26) is calculated in lines 210 to 270. The statements at lines 120 and 520 merely print out the result using 9 character values with 5 decimal places (120) or standard format (520) for the k value at 110.

```
>LIST
   20 PRINT "PROPERTIES OF THE M/M/K QUEUE"
  100 FOR K=1 TO 4
  110 PRINT"NUMBER OF SERVERS IS ";K
  120 @%=&20509
  130 PRINT"     RHO        P(0)        L        LQ        W        WQ"
  200 FOR LL=10 TO 100*K-10 STEP 10
  210 R=LL/100
  220 P=1 :S=1
  230 IF K=1 THEN GOTO 280
  240 FOR J=1 TO K-1
  250 P=P*R/J
  260 S=S+P
  270 NEXT J
  280 P=P*R:V=K-R
  290 Q=P/V
  300 S=S+Q
  400 P0=1/S
  410 LQ=R*P*P0/(V*V)
  420 L=LQ+R
  430 WQ=LQ/R
  440 W=WQ+1
  500 PRINT R,P0,L,LQ,W,WQ
  510 NEXT LL
  520 @%=10
  530 PRINT"":PRINT""
  540 NEXT K
  600 END
```

```
>RUN
PROPERTIES OF THE M/M/K QUEUE
NUMBER OF SERVERS IS 1
     RHO       P(Ø)        L         LQ         W         WQ
   0.10000   0.90000   0.11111   0.01111   1.11111   0.11111
   0.20000   0.80000   0.25000   0.05000   1.25000   0.25000
   0.30000   0.70000   0.42857   0.12857   1.42857   0.42857
   0.40000   0.60000   0.66667   0.26667   1.66667   0.66667
   0.50000   0.50000   1.00000   0.50000   2.00000   1.00000
   0.60000   0.40000   1.50000   0.90000   2.50000   1.50000
   0.70000   0.30000   2.33333   1.63333   3.33333   2.33333
   0.80000   0.20000   4.00000   3.20000   5.00000   4.00000
   0.90000   0.10000   9.00000   8.10000  10.00000   9.00000


NUMBER OF SERVERS IS 2
     RHO       P(Ø)        L         LQ         W         WQ
   0.10000   0.90476   0.10025   0.00025   1.00251   0.00251
   0.20000   0.81818   0.20202   0.00202   1.01010   0.01010
   0.30000   0.73913   0.30691   0.00691   1.02302   0.02302
   0.40000   0.66667   0.41667   0.01667   1.04167   0.04167
   0.50000   0.60000   0.53333   0.03333   1.06667   0.06667
   0.60000   0.53846   0.65934   0.05934   1.09890   0.09890
   0.70000   0.48148   0.79772   0.09772   1.13960   0.13960
   0.80000   0.42857   0.95238   0.15238   1.19048   0.19048
   0.90000   0.37931   1.12853   0.22853   1.25392   0.25392
   1.00000   0.33333   1.33333   0.33333   1.33333   0.33333
   1.10000   0.29032   1.57706   0.47706   1.43369   0.43369
   1.20000   0.25000   1.87500   0.67500   1.56250   0.56250
   1.30000   0.21212   2.25108   0.95108   1.73160   0.73160
   1.40000   0.17647   2.74510   1.34510   1.96078   0.96078
   1.50000   0.14286   3.42857   1.92857   2.28571   1.28571
   1.60000   0.11111   4.44444   2.84444   2.77778   1.77778
   1.70000   0.08108   6.12613   4.42613   3.60360   2.60360
   1.80000   0.05263   9.47368   7.67368   5.26316   4.26316
   1.90000   0.02564  19.48718  17.58718  10.25641   9.25641


NUMBER OF SERVERS IS 3
     RHO       P(Ø)        L         LQ         W         WQ
   0.10000   0.90484   0.10001   0.00001   1.00005   0.00005
   0.20000   0.81871   0.20008   0.00008   1.00042   0.00042
   0.30000   0.74074   0.30041   0.00041   1.00137   0.00137
   0.40000   0.67010   0.40127   0.00127   1.00317   0.00317
   0.50000   0.60606   0.50303   0.00303   1.00606   0.00606
   0.60000   0.54795   0.60616   0.00616   1.01027   0.01027
   0.70000   0.49516   0.71124   0.01124   1.01605   0.01605
   0.80000   0.44715   0.81892   0.01892   1.02365   0.02365
   0.90000   0.40346   0.93001   0.03001   1.03335   0.03335
   1.00000   0.36364   1.04545   0.04545   1.04545   0.04545
   1.10000   0.32730   1.16637   0.06637   1.06034   0.06034
   1.20000   0.29412   1.29412   0.09412   1.07843   0.07843
   1.30000   0.26377   1.43034   0.13034   1.10026   0.10026
   1.40000   0.23599   1.57706   0.17706   1.12647   0.12647
   1.50000   0.21053   1.73684   0.23684   1.15789   0.15789
   1.60000   0.18717   1.91291   0.31291   1.19557   0.19557
   1.70000   0.16571   2.10948   0.40948   1.24087   0.24087
   1.80000   0.14599   2.33212   0.53212   1.29562   0.29562
   1.90000   0.12783   2.58840   0.68840   1.36232   0.36232
   2.00000   0.11111   2.88889   0.88889   1.44444   0.44444
   2.10000   0.09569   3.24880   1.14880   1.54705   0.54705
   2.20000   0.08147   3.69094   1.49094   1.67770   0.67770
   2.30000   0.06833   4.25106   1.95106   1.84829   0.84829
   2.40000   0.05618   4.98876   2.58876   2.07865   1.07865
   2.50000   0.04494   6.01124   3.51124   2.40449   1.40449
   2.60000   0.03454   7.53282   4.93282   2.89724   1.89724
   2.70000   0.02491  10.05355   7.35355   3.72354   2.72354
   2.80000   0.01597  15.07348  12.27348   5.38339   4.38339
   2.90000   0.00769  30.09266  27.19266  10.37678   9.37678
```

```
NUMBER OF SERVERS IS 4
  RHO       P(0)        L         LQ         W         WQ
0.10000   0.90484   0.10000   0.00000   1.00000   0.00000
0.20000   0.81873   0.20000   0.00000   1.00002   0.00002
0.30000   0.74081   0.30002   0.00002   1.00007   0.00007
0.40000   0.67031   0.40009   0.00009   1.00022   0.00022
0.50000   0.60650   0.50026   0.00026   1.00052   0.00052
0.60000   0.54874   0.60062   0.00062   1.00103   0.00103
0.70000   0.49645   0.70128   0.00128   1.00182   0.00182
0.80000   0.44910   0.80240   0.00240   1.00299   0.00299
0.90000   0.40621   0.90416   0.00416   1.00462   0.00462
1.00000   0.36735   1.00680   0.00680   1.00680   0.00680
1.10000   0.33212   1.11060   0.01060   1.00964   0.00964
1.20000   0.30017   1.21588   0.01588   1.01323   0.01323
1.30000   0.27119   1.32302   0.02302   1.01771   0.01771
1.40000   0.24488   1.43247   0.03247   1.02319   0.02319
1.50000   0.22099   1.54475   0.04475   1.02983   0.02983
1.60000   0.19929   1.66047   0.06047   1.03779   0.03779
1.70000   0.17956   1.78033   0.08033   1.04725   0.04725
1.80000   0.16162   1.90516   0.10516   1.05842   0.05842
1.90000   0.14530   2.03597   0.13597   1.07156   0.07156
2.00000   0.13043   2.17391   0.17391   1.08696   0.08696
2.10000   0.11690   2.32042   0.22042   1.10496   0.10496
2.20000   0.10456   2.47720   0.27720   1.12600   0.12600
2.30000   0.09332   2.64637   0.34637   1.15060   0.15060
2.40000   0.08306   2.83056   0.43056   1.17940   0.17940
2.50000   0.07369   3.03309   0.53309   1.21324   0.21324
2.60000   0.06515   3.25821   0.65821   1.25316   0.25316
2.70000   0.05734   3.51145   0.81145   1.30054   0.30054
2.80000   0.05021   3.80019   1.00019   1.35721   0.35721
2.90000   0.04369   4.13447   1.23447   1.42568   0.42568
3.00000   0.03774   4.52830   1.52830   1.50943   0.50943
3.10000   0.03229   5.00194   1.90194   1.61353   0.61353
3.20000   0.02730   5.58573   2.38573   1.74554   0.74554
3.30000   0.02274   6.32732   3.02732   1.91737   0.91737
3.40000   0.01857   7.30613   3.90613   2.14886   1.14886
3.50000   0.01475   8.66503   5.16503   2.47572   1.47572
3.60000   0.01126  10.68978   7.08978   2.96938   1.96938
3.70000   0.00806  14.04708  10.34708   3.79651   2.79651
3.80000   0.00513  20.73696  16.93696   5.45709   4.45709
3.90000   0.00245  40.75945  36.85945  10.45114   9.45114
```

Exercises 3

1   Construct a full proof by induction of the result (3.6). You may assume that a steady-state solution exists.

2   Show that the single-server queue model is a special case of the birth–death model of Section 3.1. Show that the solution $p_n = (1 - \rho)\rho^n$ [where $\rho = \lambda/\mu$ in the usual notation] is a special case of equation (3.6) and that condition (3.4) leads to the requirement that $\lambda/\mu < 1$ for a steady state.

3   A single operative is in charge of a group of 3 identical machines. If a machine is running at time t the probability that it will break down in the interval $(t, t + \delta t)$ is $\lambda \delta t + \circ(\delta t)$. If the operative is free when a machine breaks down, he attends to it immediately. Otherwise he works on the machines in order of breakdown until they are all running. The time taken to repair a machine has probability density function $\mu e^{-\mu x}$; $x \geqslant 0$.
   Show that in the steady state the probability that n machines are broken down is given by

$$p_0 = p_0, \quad p_1 = 3\rho p_0, \quad p_2 = 6\rho^2 \, p_0, \quad p_3 = 6\rho^3 \, p_0$$

where $\rho = \dfrac{\lambda}{\mu}$ and find an expression for p_0.

Deduce an expression for the average number of machines running at any time.

4 Repeat Question 3 in which the operative has charge of N machines (rather than 3).
Show that

$$p_n = p_0 \frac{N!}{(N-n)!} \rho^n$$

and deduce expressions for p_0 and the average number of machines running at any time.

5 For a single-server queue with random arrivals at rate $\lambda_n = (n+2)\lambda$, and exponential service at rate $\mu_n = n\mu$, when there are n in the system, find p_n in terms of $\rho = \lambda/\mu(<1)$ and show that the expected number of customers in the system is $2\rho/(1-\rho)$.

6 Observations made over a long period show that lorries arrive at random at a loading bay at an average rate of 2 per hour. The time to load a lorry has an exponential distribution with a mean of 24 minutes.

Find the proportion of time that the loading equipment is idle and calculate the number of lorries idle (i.e. queueing or being loaded).

New equipment for loading if installed should reduce loading times by 25%. Taking into account installation, depreciation and running, the firm estimates that the additional cost of the improved facilities would be £300 per week. If an idle lorry costs £3 per hour and the lorries operate 40 hours per week would you suggest that the improvements be carried out?

7 Arrivals at a Post Office counter occur in a random manner, the average number of customers arriving per minute being C. The amount of service required by customers follows an exponential distribution but the server is very conscious of the number of customers waiting so that the average service time varies inversely as the root of the number of customers and is $k/\sqrt{n}$ where n is the number at the counter. [k is a constant.]

Under steady conditions find expressions for the probability that there are n customers at the counter. For what proportion of time is the server free?

8 In an hotel arrangements are made so that each call for room service is met immediately. If the calling rate is random with parameter λ and the service times are exponential with parameter μ, show that in the steady-state condition the probability that n members of the staff will be answering room calls has a Poisson distribution and find p_n.

9 Cars arrive randomly at rate λ, at a car park with N places. Parking times have probability density function $\mu e^{-\mu x}$; $x > 0$. Find expressions for:

(i) the probability that the park is empty,
(ii) the probability that an arriving car finds just one place available,
(iii) the proportion of arriving cars which are unable to find a place.

You should assume that when the park is full arriving cars go elsewhere immediately.

10   A service station has one pump and space for 3 cars. Cars arrive at random at an average rate of one every eight minutes. The time to serve a customer has an exponential distribution with mean 4 minutes. What proportion of potential custom is lost due to the limited waiting room?

The owner can rent some land at the side which will give him space for another car. This will cost £10 per week. If the average profit from a customer is £0.50 and the station is open 10 hours each day should he rent the land?

11   Continuation of Question 10. If the owner can install a second pump on the extra land so that he has two pumps and space for 4 cars would renting the land be profitable now?

12   A filling station employs two attendants to serve petrol, oil, etc. The time t (in minutes) to serve a customer has density function $\frac{1}{3}e^{-t/3}$ ($t > 0$) independent of the times taken on other customers.

If cars arrive at the station at random at an average rate of 20 per hour calculate:

  (i) the average number of cars at the station,
  (ii) the probability of any one car having to wait for service,
 (iii) the proportion of time for which each attendant is busy.

13   A post office counter is divided into two sections, each section being staffed by one clerk. At the first section which deals with stamps, parcels, and pensions, customers arrive at random at an average rate of 18 per hour. At the second section, which deals with postal orders, savings and licences, customers arrive at random at an average rate of 12 per hour. At both sections the service time has an exponential distribution with mean 2 minutes. What would be the effect on the average queueing time of customers for both sections, if each clerk was able to deal with the full range of customer requirements?

14   The work study group in a factory report that the average number of lorries waiting in the factory's one unloading bay is 4.0. (This includes the one being unloaded.)

The yard in which the bay is situated becomes congested if more than 6 lorries are in it at any one time. Find the proportion of time the yard is congested.

If a second identical bay is built in the yard estimate the average number of lorries waiting when both bays are in operation. This second bay reduces available space so that congestion will occur if more than 4 lorries are in the yard at any one time. Estimate the proportion of time that this will occur.

State clearly the assumptions you make.

15   There are two inspectors who check the work of other workers. The work arrives at random at an average rate of 6 pieces per hour and it takes on average 15 minutes for an inspector to check a piece, the inspection time having an exponential distribution.

Find the proportion of time that (i) both inspectors are free, (ii) one inspector is free.

How long must a workman wait (on average) when he takes his work to be inspected?

16   Show (along the lines given in Sections 2.3 and 3.3) that

$$\phi_k(x) = \frac{\mu p_0}{(k-1)!}\left(\frac{\lambda}{\mu}\right)^k e^{-(k\mu-\lambda)x}; \quad x > 0$$

as given by equation (3.31).

Deduce that

$$\int_0^\infty \phi_k(x)\,\mathrm{d}x = 1 - \Pr(X=0)$$

where $\Pr(X=0)$ is given by equation (3.30).

17   An hotel foyer has 2 telephone booths for use by its clients. Callers arrive at random at an average rate of 20 per hour. Calls have an exponential life with mean 5 minutes. Find the probability that (i) no booths are in use, (ii) 1 booth is in use, (iii) both booths are in use. Find the average number of booths in use.

If a third booth is installed find the average number of booths in use.

18   For the M/M/k system show that the average number of occupied servers is ρ.

19   Use the result of Question 18 to develop an argument which shows that for the M/M/k system, $L = L_q + \rho$.

20   For the M/M/k system let Y be the time spent in the system and let Y have probability density function $\psi_k(y)$ and distribution function $\Psi_k(y)$.

Show that

$$\Psi_k(y) = 1 - e^{-\mu y} - \frac{\mu^2 \left(\dfrac{\lambda}{\mu}\right)^k p_0}{(k-1)!\,(k\mu-\lambda)[(k-1)\,\mu-\lambda]}\left[e^{-\mu y} - e^{-(k\mu-\lambda)y}\right].$$

Deduce that

$$E(Y) = W = \frac{\mu\left(\dfrac{\lambda}{\mu}\right)^k}{(k-1)!\,(k\mu-\lambda)^2}\,p_0 + \frac{1}{\mu},$$

in accord with equation (3.33).

21   For the M/M/k system for $k = 1, 2, \ldots, 10$ write a BASIC program to calculate

$$\Pr(N=n) \quad \text{for } n = 0, 1, \ldots, 10,$$

and

$$\Pr(N \leqslant n) \quad \text{for } n = 0, 1, \ldots, 10,$$

for values of $\rho = \dfrac{\lambda}{\mu}$.

4
Further Models for the Single-Server Queue

4.1 The M/G/1 Queue

We consider in this section the single-server queue with random arrivals at an average rate λ and service times which are independently and identically distributed with probability density function $b(t)$; $t \geqslant 0$.

It was pointed out in Section 2.2, where service times were assumed to have a negative exponential distribution, that it was only in this case that the approach by way of equations (2.16), (2.17) and (2.18), which led to the set of differential equations, (2.19), was valid. For any other distribution of service times, the probability that a service (in progress at time t) will terminate in $(t, t + \delta t)$ will depend on t as well as δt. This simple fact (the failure of equation (1.19) to hold for distributions other than the negative exponential) means that we have to abandon the approach of Section 2.2 in the case of a general service time distribution.

We follow the argument of D. G. Kendall. Label the customers in sequence, 1, 2, ..., n, ... Let q_n be the number of customers left in the system at the instant when the service of customer n terminates. Let ζ_n be the number of customers who arrive during the service time of customer n. q_n and ζ_n are random variables and it is clear that ζ_1, ζ_2, ..., ζ_n are independent identically distributed random variables (the service times are independent) and that further ζ_n is independent of $q_0, q_1, \ldots, q_{n-1}$.

Consider the state of the system when customer n leaves and again when customer $n+1$ leaves.

For $q_n > 0$,
$$q_{n+1} = q_n - 1 + \zeta_{n+1} \qquad (4.1)$$
but if $q_n = 0$,
$$q_{n+1} = \zeta_{n+1}. \qquad (4.2)$$
This is clear from Figs 4.1 (a) and (b).

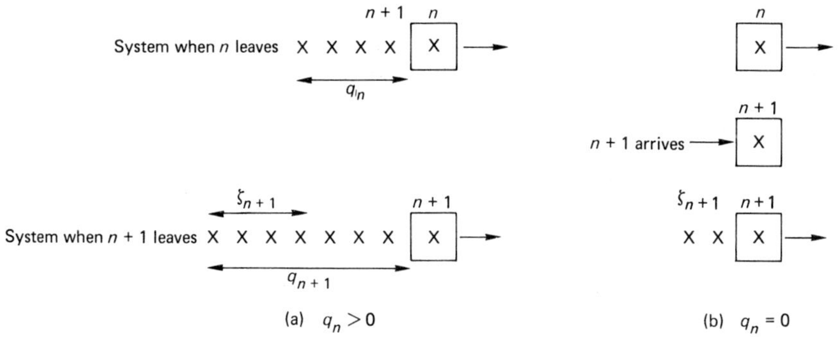

Fig. 4.1

We can combine equations (4.1) and (4.2) into the one result

$$q_{n+1} = q_n - U(q_n) + \zeta_{n+1} \tag{4.3}$$

where

$$U(q_n) = 1; \quad q_n > 0$$

$$= 0; \quad q_n = 0.$$

$U(x)$ defined by $\left.\begin{array}{l} U(x) = 1; \quad x > 0 \\ = 0; \quad x \leqslant 0 \end{array}\right\}$ is the Heaviside unit-step function.

Its graph is shown in Fig. 4.2.

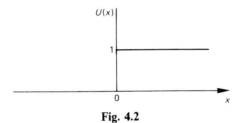

Fig. 4.2

Of course q_n only takes on discrete values in our problem and equation (4.3) is the fundamental relationship between the random variables q_{n+1}, q_n and ζ_{n+1}.

For the random variable ζ_r (they all have the same distribution independent of r), if the service time of customer r is t, then ζ_r will have a Poisson distribution with mean λt (equation (1.3)).

Thus

$$\Pr(\zeta_r = k|t) = \frac{e^{-\lambda t}(\lambda t)^k}{k!} \tag{4.4}$$

This gives the distribution of the number of customers to arrive during the service time of customer r, given that the service time is t. Thus for the conditional expectations we shall have

$$E\{\zeta_r|t\} = \lambda t, \quad E\{\zeta_r^2|t\} = \lambda t + (\lambda t)^2, \quad \mathrm{Var}\{\zeta_r|t\} = \lambda t. \tag{4.5}$$

Then for the unconditional expectations

$$E\{\zeta_r\} = \int_0^\infty \lambda t\, b(t)\, \mathrm{d}t = \lambda b = \rho \tag{4.6}$$

and

$$E\{\zeta_r^2\} = \int_0^\infty (\lambda t + \lambda^2\, t^2)\, b(t)\, \mathrm{d}t = \lambda b + \lambda^2\, E\{T^2\} \tag{4.7}$$

where $b = \int_0^\infty tb(t)\, \mathrm{d}t$ is the mean service time.

But
$$E\{T^2\} = \mathrm{Var}\{T\} + [E\{T\}]^2$$
$$= \mathrm{Var}\{T\} + b^2$$
$$\therefore \quad E\{\zeta_r^2\} = \lambda b + \lambda^2 b^2 + \lambda^2 \,\mathrm{Var}\{T\} \tag{4.8}$$

where $\mathrm{Var}\{T\}$ is the variance of the service time.

On taking the expected value on both sides of equation (4.3) we obtain
$$E\{q_{n+1}\} = E\{q_n\} - E\{U(q_n)\} + E\{\zeta_{n+1}\}. \tag{4.9}$$

Now if we assume that a steady-state situation arises as $n \to \infty$, the distributions of q_n and q_{n+1} will be identical when a large number of customers have been served. In this situation
$$\mathrm{Lim}_{n \to \infty} \mathrm{Pr}(q_n = k) = \pi_k \text{ say.} \tag{4.10}$$

Thus $E\{q_n\} = E\{q_{n+1}\}$ so that equation (4.9) yields
$$E\{U(q_n)\} = E\{\zeta_{n+1}\} = \lambda b = \rho \tag{4.11}$$

on using equation (4.6).

Our earlier discussion on the steady-state situation would lead us to expect a steady state to exist provided $\lambda b = \rho < 1$ and this indeed is the case. π_k can then be interpreted as the probability that a customer leaves behind k in the system, or as the proportion of customers who leave k behind in the system.

For the result (4.11) we realise that $U(q_n)$ takes on just two values. $U(q_n) = 0$ if $q_n = 0$ and this event will have probability π_0. $U(q_n) = 1$ if $q_n > 0$ and this event will have probability $1 - \pi_0$. Thus
$$E\{U(q_n)\} = \pi_0 \times 0 + (1 - \pi_0)\,1 = 1 - \pi_0.$$
$$\therefore \quad 1 - \pi_0 = \rho \quad \text{(from equation (4.11))}$$
$$\therefore \quad \pi_0 = 1 - \rho = 1 - \lambda b. \tag{4.12}$$

Thus the probability that a departing customer leaves behind an empty system is $1 - \rho$. Thus must also be the probability that an arriving customer finds an empty system and so does not have to wait in a queue for service.

This result and its interpretation should be compared with equation (2.24) $[p_0 = 1 - \rho]$ for negative exponential service and equation (2.32) for the queueing time. Of course p_0 refers to the probability that the system is empty at an arbitrary moment in time, whereas π_0 is the probability that the system is left empty at the moment of departure of a customer.

We can derive $E\{q_n\}$ from equation (4.3). First square this result to obtain
$$q_{n+1}^2 = q_n^2 + [U(q_n)]^2 + \zeta_{n+1}^2 + 2q_n \zeta_{n+1} - 2q_n U(q_n) - 2\zeta_{n+1} U(q_n)$$
$$\therefore \quad q_{n+1}^2 = q_n^2 + U(q_n) + \zeta_{n+1}^2 + 2q_n \zeta_{n+1} - 2q_n - 2\zeta_{n+1} U(q_n)$$

since $[U(q_n)]^2 = U(q_n)$ and $q_n U(q_n) = q_n$.

Thus
$$E\{q_{n+1}^2\} = E\{q_n^2\} + E\{U(q_n)\} + E\{\zeta_{n+1}^2\} + 2E\{q_n \zeta_{n+1}\} - 2E\{q_n\} - 2E\{\zeta_{n+1} U(q_n)\}.$$

Now in the steady state, $E\{q_{n+1}^2\} = E\{q_n^2\}$, and since ζ_{n+1} is independent of q_n and hence of $U(q_n)$,

$$E\{q_n \zeta_{n+1}\} = E\{q_n\} E\{\zeta_{n+1}\} \quad \text{and} \quad E\{\zeta_{n+1} U(q_n)\} = E\{\zeta_{n+1}\} E\{U(q_n)\}.$$

Thus we obtain

$$0 = E\{U(q_n)\} + E\{\zeta_{n+1}^2\} + 2E\{q_n\} E\{\zeta_{n+1}\} - 2E\{q_n\} - 2E\{\zeta_{n+1}\} E\{U(q_n)\}.$$

Whence, if we substitute from equations (4.11), (4.6) and (4.8) we obtain after a little algebra

$$2E\{q_n\}(1 - \rho) = \rho + \rho + \rho^2 + \lambda^2 \, \text{Var}\{T\} - 2\rho^2.$$

$$\therefore \quad E\{q_n\} = \frac{2\rho - 2\rho^2 + \rho^2 + \lambda^2 \, \text{Var}\{T\}}{2(1 - \rho)}.$$

$$\therefore \quad E\{q_n\} = \rho + \frac{\rho^2 + \lambda^2 \, \text{Var}\{T\}}{2(1 - \rho)}. \tag{4.13}$$

This gives the mean value for the number of customers left behind by a departing customer. It is interesting to note that it depends on the service time, only through the mean of that distribution ($\rho = \lambda b$), and the variance of the distribution which appears in equation (4.13) directly. Thus in order to reduce the average number left in the system for a given arrival rate we can see the advantages in reducing the mean service time. However, even if no reduction in the mean service time is possible we can still reduce $E\{q_n\}$ if we can reduce the variance of the service time. Other properties of the service time distribution, apart from the mean and variance, do not effect the value of $E\{q_n\}$.

Example 1

Apply equation (4.13) to the cases of (i) negative exponential service time with mean $1/\mu$, (ii) constant service time with mean $1/\mu$.

(i) If T, the service time, has a negative exponential distribution with mean $1/\mu$ ($\equiv b$ in equation (4.6)), then $\text{Var}\{T\} = 1/\mu^2$.
In this case equation (4.13) takes the form

$$E\{q_n\} = \rho + \frac{\rho^2 + \rho^2}{2(1 - \rho)} = \rho + \frac{2\rho^2}{2(1 - \rho)} = \frac{\rho}{1 - \rho}. \tag{4.14}$$

(ii) In the case of constant service time, $\text{Var}\{T\} = 0$ so that from equation (4.13)

$$E\{q_n\} = \rho + \frac{\rho^2}{2(1 - \rho)}. \tag{4.15}$$

Thus we see by comparing equation (4.14) with equation (2.28) that in the case of random arrivals and negative exponential service the average number in the system at an arbitrary moment in time (2.28) is equal to the average number in the system at the moments of departure. It is not clear intuitively why this should be so. It is only true for random arrivals.

We also note on comparing equation (4.15) with equation (4.14) that the reduction in the $\text{Var}\{T\}$ to zero has led to a reduction in $\text{E}\{q_n\}$ of $\dfrac{\rho^2}{2(1-\rho)}$.

If the nth customer spends time Y in the system, then q_n is the number of customers who join the queue during this time period of length Y.

$$\therefore \quad \text{E}\{q_n|Y\} = \lambda Y$$

so that
$$\text{E}\{q_n\} = \lambda \text{E}\{Y\} = \lambda W \tag{4.16}$$

$$\therefore \quad \text{E}\{Y\} = W = \frac{\text{E}\{q_n\}}{\lambda}. \tag{4.17}$$

These results may be compared with the formula $L = \lambda W$ (Question 14, Exercises 2) for negative exponential service times.

$$\therefore \quad \text{E}\{Y\} = W = b + \frac{1}{\lambda}\left[\frac{\rho^2 + \lambda^2 \text{Var}\{T\}}{2(1-\rho)}\right]. \tag{4.18}$$

Of course if X is the time spent in the queue by a customer and T is his or her service time, then Y, the time spent in the system, is given by

$$Y = X + T$$

$$\therefore \quad \text{E}\{Y\} = \text{E}\{X\} + \text{E}\{T\} = W_q + b.$$

It follows that W_q (the mean queueing time) is given by

$$W_q = \frac{1}{\lambda}\left[\frac{\rho^2 + \lambda^2 \text{Var}\{T\}}{2(1-\rho)}\right]. \tag{4.19}$$

The results (4.15), (4.18) and (4.19) are sometimes referred to as the Pollaczek–Khinchtine formulae.

Our results so far have enabled us to evaluate the expected values of some of the important random variables associated with the queueing system under discussion. We can by ingenious use of equation (4.3) find the distribution of q_n in the steady state, as given by the probabilities π_k;

$$\Pr(q_n = k) = \pi_k$$

at equation (4.10).

Let $Q(z) = \sum\limits_{k=0}^{\infty} \pi_k z^k = \text{E}\{z^{q_n}\} = \text{E}\{z^{q_{n+1}}\}$ be the generating function for the π_ks.
Then from equation (4.3)

$$Q(z) = \text{E}\{z^{q_n - U(q_n) + \zeta_{n+1}}\}$$
$$= \text{E}\{z^{q_n - U(q_n)}\} \cdot \text{E}\{z^{\zeta_{n+1}}\} \tag{4.20}$$

since ζ_{n+1} and q_n are independent.

Denote for the time being $\text{E}\{z^{\zeta_{n+1}}\}$ by $\Phi(z)$.

Now $\text{E}\{z^{q_n - U(q_n)}\} = \pi_0 + \pi_1 z^{1-1} + \pi_2 z^{2-1} + \pi_3 z^{3-1} + \ldots$ in view of the definition of $U(q_n)$ which is 1 for $q_n > 0$.

$$\therefore \quad \mathrm{E}\{z^{q_n - U(q_n)}\} = \pi_0 + \sum_{r=1}^{\infty} \pi_r z^{r-1}$$

$$= \pi_0 + \frac{Q(z) - \pi_0}{z}$$

$$\therefore \quad Q(z) = \varPhi(z)\left[\pi_0 + \frac{Q(z) - \pi_0}{z}\right]$$

$$\therefore \quad Q(z) = \frac{\pi_0(1-z)\,\varPhi(z)}{\varPhi(z) - z}$$

after a little algebra, and since $\pi_0 = (1-\rho)$,

$$Q(z) = \frac{(1-\rho)(1-z)\,\varPhi(z)}{\varPhi(z) - z}. \tag{4.21}$$

There remains the task of determining $\varPhi(z)$

$$\varPhi(z) = \mathrm{E}\{z^{\zeta_{n+1}}\} = \sum_{k=0}^{\infty} z^k \, \mathrm{Pr}(\zeta_{n+1} = k).$$

$$\mathrm{Pr}(\zeta_{n+1} = k) = \int_0^{\infty} \frac{\mathrm{e}^{-\lambda t}(\lambda t)^k}{k!}\, b(t)\, \mathrm{d}t \quad \text{from equation (4.4).} \tag{4.22}$$

$$\therefore \quad \varPhi(z) = \sum_{k=0}^{\infty} z^k \int_0^{\infty} \frac{\mathrm{e}^{-\lambda t}(\lambda t)^k}{k!}\, b(t)\, \mathrm{d}t$$

$$= \int_0^{\infty} \mathrm{e}^{-\lambda t}\, b(t) \left(\sum_{k=0}^{\infty} \frac{(\lambda t z)^k}{k!} \right) \mathrm{d}t$$

$$= \int_0^{\infty} \mathrm{e}^{-\lambda t(1-z)}\, b(t)\, \mathrm{d}t.$$

$$\therefore \quad \varPhi(z) = B^*[\lambda(1-z)] \tag{4.23}$$

where

$$B^*(s) = \int_0^{\infty} \mathrm{e}^{-st}\, b(t)\, \mathrm{d}t \tag{4.24}$$

is the Laplace Transform of $b(t)$.

Of course if we can find $Q(z)$ as a function of z, we can, by expanding $Q(z)$ as a power series, find π_k as the coefficient of z^k. Given the service time distribution $b(t)$, equation (4.23) enables us to find $\varPhi(z)$ and then equation (4.21) yields $Q(z)$. In the case of the M/M/1 queue with negative exponential service

$$B^*(s) = \int_0^{\infty} \mu\, \mathrm{e}^{-st}\, \mathrm{e}^{-\mu t}\, \mathrm{d}t = \frac{\mu}{\mu + s}$$

[see also equation (1.12)].

Thus

$$\Phi(z) = \frac{\mu}{\mu + \lambda(1-z)} = \frac{1}{1 + \rho(1-z)} \quad \text{where } \rho = \frac{\lambda}{\mu}.$$

$$\therefore \quad Q(z) = \frac{(1-\rho)(1-z)}{1+\rho(1-z)} \cdot \left[\frac{1}{\dfrac{1}{1+\rho(1-z)} - z} \right]$$

$$= \frac{(1-\rho)(1-z)}{1 - z - \rho z(1-z)} = \frac{1-\rho}{1-\rho z}$$

$$= (1-\rho)(1 + \rho z + \rho^2 z^2 + \cdots + \rho^k z^k + \cdots).$$

$$\therefore \quad \pi_k = (1-\rho)\rho^k \quad [= p_k \text{ of equation (2.25)}].$$

Thus the number in the system at a moment of departure has the same distribution as the number in the system at an arbitrary moment.

We can also investigate the distribution of the time Y spent in the system by the nth customer in the steady state. Let this have probability density function $f(y)$. Then q_n is the number of customers who arrive during the time spent in the system by customer n.

$$\therefore \quad \Pr(q_n = k) = \pi_k = \int_0^\infty \frac{e^{-\lambda y}(\lambda y)^k}{k!} f(y)\, dy$$

by an argument identical to that used in deriving equation (4.22).

Thus

$$Q(z) = \Sigma \pi_k z^k = \sum_{k=0}^{\infty} z^k \int_0^\infty \frac{e^{-\lambda y}(\lambda y)^k}{k!} f(y)\, dy$$

$$\therefore \quad Q(z) = \int_0^\infty e^{-\lambda y(1-z)} f(y)\, dy$$

$$\therefore \quad Q(z) = F^*[\lambda(1-z)]$$

where $F^*(s) = \int_0^\infty e^{-sy} f(y)\, dy$ is the Laplace Transform of $f(y)$. [Compare equation (4.23).]

$$\therefore \quad \text{From equations (4.21) and (4.23)}$$

$$Q(z) = \frac{(1-\rho)(1-z)\, B^*[\lambda(1-z)]}{B^*[\lambda(1-z)] - z} = F^*[\lambda(1-z)].$$

Thus with $s = \lambda(1-z)$, i.e. $z = 1 - \dfrac{s}{\lambda}$

$$F^*(s) = \frac{\dfrac{(1-\rho)s}{\lambda} B^*(s)}{B^*(s) + \dfrac{s}{\lambda} - 1}$$

$$\therefore \quad F^*(s) = \frac{(1-\rho)\, s B^*(s)}{s - \lambda + \lambda B^*(s)} \tag{4.25}$$

This gives the Laplace Transform of $f(y)$. Readers familiar with the methods for inverting Laplace Transforms will know that $f(y)$ can be obtained from $F^*(s)$ as

$$f(y) = \frac{1}{2\pi i} \int_{c-i\infty}^{c-i\infty} e^{sy}\, F^*(s)\, \mathrm{d}s. \tag{4.26}$$

In the case of negative exponential service $B^*(s) = \dfrac{\mu}{\mu + s}$.

$$\therefore \quad F^*(s) = \frac{(\mu - \lambda)\, s\mu}{\mu(s+\mu)} \bigg/ \left(s - \lambda + \frac{\lambda\mu}{\mu + s} \right)$$

$$\therefore \quad F^*(s) = \frac{\mu - \lambda}{\mu - \lambda + s}$$

and we recognise from the form of $F^*(s)$ that

$$f(y) = (\mu - \lambda)\, e^{-(\mu - \lambda) y}; \quad y \geqslant 0.$$

[Compare $F^*(s)$ with $B^*(s)$ above.]

This result is of course in accord with equation (2.37). In this particular case, because we recognise the Laplace Transform as a 'standard form' there is no problem with its inversion. However, even if we cannot find $f(y)$ very easily from $F^*(s)$, by expanding the latter as a power series in s we can derive the moments of Y. The coefficient of $-s$ will give $\mathrm{E}\{Y\}$ and the coefficient of $\dfrac{(-s)^r}{r!}$ will give $\mathrm{E}(Y^r)$.

If X is the time spent in the queue and T is the service time of a customer then X and T are independent and

$$Y = X + T$$

Thus
$$F^*(s) = V^*(s)\, B^*(s)$$

where $V^*(s)$ is the Laplace Transform of the queueing time distribution.

Hence

$$V^*(s) = \frac{(1-\rho)\, s}{s - \lambda + \lambda B^*(s)} \tag{4.27}$$

Care needs to be exercised in using equation (4.27). The distribution of X is part discrete $[\Pr(X = 0) = 1 - \rho]$ and part continuous with density function $\phi(x)$.

Hence

$$V^*(s) = \mathrm{E}\{e^{-sX}\} = e^{-s.0}\, \Pr(X = 0) + \int_0^\infty e^{-sx}\, \phi(x)\, \mathrm{d}x$$

$$= (1 - \rho) + \int_0^\infty e^{-sx}\, \phi(x)\, \mathrm{d}x$$

$$= (1 - \rho) + \Phi^*(s) \tag{4.28}$$

where
$$\Phi^*(s) = \int_0^\infty e^{-sx} \phi(x) \, dx$$

so that $\phi(x) = \dfrac{1}{2\pi i} \displaystyle\int_{c-i\infty}^{c+i\infty} e^{sx} \Phi^*(s) \, ds$ if the inversion formula is used to find the

density function, which we must remember is only part of the distribution.

4.2 The Imbedded Markov Process

Many of the results of the previous section can be obtained using the idea of the imbedded Markov process. This latter idea transcends our particular problem and has wider applications.

We have noted earlier that when arrivals occur at random the arrival process is an ongoing process through time (unlike service which only proceeds when there are customers present). Thus when a customer leaves the system on the completion of his service the state of the system can be·adequately described by the number of customers left in the system and this number determines the future behaviour of the system. The system changes from one state (described by the number present) to another at the completion of successive services. The arrivals which occur between these services determine the changes that occur. Such a process is an example of a Markov process. (In fact the M in our description M/M/1 is M for Markovian.)

The instants of service completion are known as points of regeneration of the process. We do not worry about the precise moments in time at which they occur. The state of the system at such an instant is described by the number k where k is the number of customers left in the system. Now we have seen that for the M/G/1 system, provided $\rho = \lambda b < 1$, the system will eventually reach a steady-state (equilibrium or stationary) situation with

$$\Pr(\text{State } k) = \underset{n \to \infty}{\text{Limit}} \Pr(q_n = k) = \pi_k.$$

Now for random arrivals at average rate λ the probability that j customers arrive during a service time is

$$\Pr(\zeta_n = j) = r_j = \int_0^\infty \frac{e^{-\lambda t}(\lambda t)^j}{j!} b(t) \, dt. \quad \text{[See equation (4.22).]} \qquad (4.29)$$

The r_j give the probabilities for the various transitions that occur during the successive service times.

Thus we obtain

$$\pi_0 = \pi_0 \, r_0 + \pi_1 \, r_0. \qquad (4.30)$$

The system is left empty by customer n (with probability π_0) if it is left empty by customer $(n-1)$, (with probability π_0) and no customers arrive during the service time of customer n (with probability r_0), even though this service only commences with his arrival, or, customer $(n-1)$ leaves 1 in the system (customer n), with probability π_1 and no customers arrive during his service time. Also

$$\pi_1 = \pi_0 \, r_1 + \pi_1 \, r_1 + \pi_2 \, r_0 \qquad (4.31)$$

Customer n leaves 1 customer behind if customer $(n-1)$ leaves 0 or 1 behind and 1 customer arrives during the service time of customer n, or customer $(n-1)$ leaves two customers behind, (viz. n and $(n+1)$), and no customers arrive during the service time of customer n.

Continuing in this way we derive in turn

$$\pi_2 = \pi_0\, r_2 + \pi_1\, r_2 + \pi_2\, r_1 + \pi_3\, r_0$$

$$\pi_3 = \pi_0\, r_3 + \pi_1\, r_3 + \pi_2\, r_2 + \pi_3\, r_1 + \pi_4\, r_0$$

etc.

These equations can be written in Markov chain notation as

$$\pi^{\mathrm{T}} = \pi^{\mathrm{T}}\, R \tag{4.32}$$

where

$$\pi^{\mathrm{T}} = (\pi_0, \pi_1, \ldots, \pi_k, \ldots)$$

is the steady-state probability row vector, and

$$R = \begin{pmatrix} r_0 & r_1 & r_2 & r_3 & r_4 & \cdots \\ r_0 & r_1 & r_2 & r_3 & r_4 & \cdots \\ & r_0 & r_1 & r_2 & r_3 & \cdots \\ & & r_0 & r_1 & r_2 & \cdots \\ & & & r_0 & r_1 & \cdots \\ & & & & r_0 & \cdots \end{pmatrix}$$

is the transition matrix.

We define as before

$$Q(z) = \sum_{k=0}^{\infty} \pi_k\, z^k$$

and

$$\Phi(z) = \sum_{k=0}^{\infty} r_k\, z^k = B^*[\lambda(1-z)]$$

from equation (4.23).

Then we can write our equations as

$$\pi_0 = \pi_0\, r_0 + \pi_1\, r_0 \qquad\qquad \times z^0$$

$$\pi_1 = \pi_0\, r_1 + \pi_1\, r_1 + \pi_2\, r_0 \qquad \times z^1$$

$$\pi_2 = \pi_0\, r_2 + \pi_1\, r_2 + \pi_2\, r_1 + \pi_3\, r_0 \times z^2$$

etc.

Multiplication of the successive equations by z^0, z^1, z^2 etc. followed by addition gives

$$Q(z) = (\pi_0 + \pi_1 + \pi_2\, z + \pi_3\, z^2 + \cdots)\, \Phi(z)$$

$$= \left\{ \pi_0 + \frac{Q(z) - \pi_0}{z} \right\} \Phi(z)$$

whence, after a little algebra

$$Q(z) = \frac{\pi_0(1-z)\,\Phi(z)}{\Phi(z) - z}. \tag{4.33}$$

This is equivalent to equation (4.21) although the value $\pi_0 = (1 - \rho)$ has been included in the latter.

We can deduce the value for π_0 by using the condition

$$Q(1) = \pi_0 + \pi_1 + \cdots = 1.$$

$\Phi(1)$ is 1 so that for the right hand side of equation (4.33) as $z \to 1$ we obtain (L'Hopital's rule)

$$1 = \frac{-\pi_0}{\Phi'(1) - 1}$$

$$\therefore \quad \pi_0 = 1 - \Phi'(1) = 1 - \int_0^\infty e^{-\lambda t}\, b(t) \sum_{k=1}^\infty \frac{(\lambda t)^k}{(k-1)!}\, dt$$

$$= 1 - \int_0^\infty \lambda t b(t)\, dt = 1 - \rho$$

as before.

4.3 The G/M/1 Queue

We can deal with the single-server queue with the assumption of negative exponential service times, but a general distribution for the inter-arrival times, by the method of the previous section. Thus we assume that service times have a negative exponential distribution with probability density function $\mu e^{-\mu t}$; $t \geqslant 0$. It is further assumed that the inter-arrival times for the successive customers are independent identically distributed random variables with probability density function $a(t)$; $t \geqslant 0$.

For this problem we consider the system at those moments when a customer arrives. We let Q_n denote the number of customers already in the system as customer n arrives. We assume the existence of a steady-state situation as $n \to \infty$ so that we denote

$$\lim_{n \to \infty} \Pr(Q_n = k) = u_k.$$

The state of the system at the arrival moments is described by the value of Q_n. The transitions that occur in the successive values of Q_n and Q_{n+1} will depend on the number of service completions that have occurred in the inter-arrival time. We let v_j denote the probability that exactly j customers are served in an inter-arrival interval given that service continues throughout the interval.

Then
$$v_j = \int_0^\infty \frac{e^{-\mu t}(\mu t)^j}{j!}\,.\,a(t)\, dt. \tag{4.34}$$

This is derived by the same argument that led to equation (4.22) from (4.4). Of course the assumption of negative exponential service is crucial. It is also convenient to introduce

$$t_j = 1 - \sum_{i=0}^{j} v_i \qquad (4.35)$$

to denote the probability that more than j customers can be served in an inter-arrival interval.

Then in the steady-state situation

$$u_0 = u_0 \, t_0 + u_1 \, t_1 + u_2 \, t_2 + \cdots$$

$$u_1 = u_0 \, v_0 + u_1 \, v_1 + u_2 \, v_2 + \cdots$$

$$u_2 = u_1 \, v_0 + u_2 \, v_1 + u_3 \, v_2 + \cdots \qquad (4.36)$$

$$u_3 = u_2 \, v_0 + u_3 \, v_1 + u_4 \, v_2 + \cdots$$

$$\text{etc.}$$

i.e.
$$u_k = \sum_{i=0}^{\infty} u_{i+k-1} \, v_i, \quad k = 1, 2, 3, \ldots \qquad (4.37)$$

along with
$$u_0 = u_0 \, t_0 + u_1 \, t_1 + u_2 \, t_2 + \cdots \qquad (4.38)$$

These equations can be written in the form

$$(u_0, u_1, \ldots, u_k, \ldots) = (u_0, u_1, \ldots, u_k, \ldots) \, V$$

where the transition matrix

$$V = \begin{pmatrix} t_0 & v_0 & 0 & 0 & 0 & \cdots \\ t_1 & v_1 & v_0 & 0 & 0 & \cdots \\ t_2 & v_2 & v_1 & v_0 & 0 & \cdots \\ t_3 & v_3 & v_2 & v_1 & v_0 & \cdots \\ t_4 & v_4 & v_3 & v_2 & v_1 & \cdots \\ \cdot & \cdot & \cdot & \cdot & \cdot & \cdots \\ \cdot & \cdot & \cdot & \cdot & \cdot & \cdots \\ \cdot & \cdot & \cdot & \cdot & \cdot & \cdots \end{pmatrix}$$

is a Markovian matrix. The sum of the elements in each row is 1 and of course all elements are positive.

For the equation with $k = 1$, the $(n+1)$th customer will find 1 in the system on arrival if the nth customer found 0 and his service was not completed in the inter-arrival time, (customer n is the one found by customer $(n+1)$ of course), or the nth customer found 1 and there was 1 service completion in the inter-arrival time, or the nth customer found 2 and there were 2 service completions in the inter-arrival time etc. Summing the probabilities for these mutually exclusive events gives the right hand side. A similar argument holds for all values of k except $k = 0$.

The argument to establish the first equation is a little more tricky. Customer $(n+1)$ will find the system empty if the customer n found k in the system on arrival, and these k along with customer n were served during the inter-arrival time. But of course once the system becomes empty service ceases, so we cannot use v_{k+1} for this probability since that would assume that service was going on throughout the interval. Suppose the inter-arrival interval is t. Then the sum of $(k+1)$ negative exponential variables is a random variable X with probability density function

$$g(x) = \mu \frac{(\mu x)^k \, e^{-\mu k}}{k!} \qquad \text{[compare with equation (1.13)]}.$$

The probability that $X \leqslant t$ is what is required. This is

$$\int_0^t \mu \frac{(\mu x)^k \, e^{-\mu x}}{k!} = \sum_{j=k+1}^{\infty} \frac{(\mu t)^j \, e^{-\mu t}}{j!}$$

as repeated integration by parts readily shows.
Thus

$$\Pr(X \leqslant t) = 1 - \sum_{j=0}^{k} \frac{(\mu t)^j \, e^{-\mu t}}{j!} \tag{4.39}$$

Thus the probability that these $(k+1)$ customers are served within the given interval is given by equation (4.39). But t is a random variable. Thus the probability that the customers are served within the inter-arrival time is

$$\int_0^{\infty} \left[1 - \sum_{j=0}^{k} \frac{(\mu t)^j \, e^{-\mu t}}{j!} \right] a(t) \, dt = 1 - \sum_{j=0}^{k} v_j = t_k \quad \text{as required.}$$

Of course we can also take the view that equation (4.38) says nothing new! The R.H.S. of (4.38) can be written as

$$u_0(1 - v_0)$$
$$+ u_1(1 - v_0 - v_1)$$
$$+ u_2(1 - v_0 - v_1 - v_2)$$

etc.

$$= u_0 + u_1 + u_2 + \cdots$$
$$- (u_0 \, v_0 + u_1 \, v_1 + u_2 \, v_2 + \cdots)$$
$$- (u_1 \, v_0 + u_2 \, v_1 + u_3 \, v_2 + \cdots)$$
$$- (u_2 \, v_0 + u_3 \, v_1 + \cdots)$$

etc.

$$= 1 - u_1 - u_2 - u_3 - \cdots$$
$$= u_0$$

which is the L.H.S.

For the system of equations (4.36) a solution exists which is of the form

$$u_k = \alpha + \beta\eta^k \tag{4.40}$$

where α, β and η are constants to be found.

For the equation with $k = 1$, direct substitution gives

$$\alpha + \beta\eta = \sum_{i=0}^{\infty} \alpha v_i + \beta \sum_{i=0}^{\infty} v_i\,\eta^i$$

i.e.

$$\alpha + \beta\eta = \alpha + \beta P(\eta)$$

where $P(z) = \sum_{i=0}^{\infty} v_i z^i$ is the generating function for the v_i.

For a general value for k

$$\alpha + \beta\eta^k = \alpha \sum_{i=0}^{\infty} v_i + \beta \sum_{i=0}^{\infty} v_i\,\eta^{i+k-1}$$

i.e.

$$\alpha + \beta\eta^k = \alpha + \beta\eta^{k-1}\, P(\eta).$$

Thus $u_k = \alpha + \beta\eta^k$ is a solution provided

$$\eta = P(\eta). \tag{4.41}$$

Of course since $\sum_{k=0}^{\infty} u_k = 1$ we must have $\alpha = 0$ and $\eta < 1$ for the series to be convergent. We can understand the conclusion concerning α from consideration of the first equation ($k = 0$).

$$\begin{aligned}
u_0 = \alpha + \beta = \quad & (\alpha + \beta)(1 - v_0) \\
& + (\alpha + \beta\eta)(1 - v_0 - v_1) \\
& + (\alpha + \beta\eta^2)(1 - v_0 - v_1 - v_2)
\end{aligned}$$

etc.

$$\therefore \quad \alpha + \beta = \alpha \sum_{j=0}^{\infty} t_j + \frac{\beta}{1-\eta} - \frac{\beta v_0}{1-\eta} - \frac{\beta v_1\,\eta}{1-\eta} - \frac{\beta v_2\,\eta^2}{1-\eta} - \cdots$$

i.e.

$$\alpha + \beta = \alpha \sum_{j=0}^{\infty} t_j + \frac{(1 - P(\eta))}{1-\eta}\,\beta$$

so that if $\eta = P(\eta)$ we should have

$$\alpha = \alpha \sum_{j=0}^{\infty} t_j \quad \text{whence } \alpha = 0.$$

The condition that $\eta < 1$ implies that η is the smallest root of the equation

$$z = P(z) \tag{4.42}$$

and that

$$P'(1) > 1. \tag{4.43}$$

$z = 1$ is a solution of (4.42), and equation (4.43) is the condition that there is a root of (4.42) which is less than 1 (Fig. 4.3). Equation (4.43) is the condition that a steady-state solution exists. Since

$$P'(1) = \sum_{i=0}^{\infty} i v_i$$

it represents the mean number of services completed in an inter-arrival interval. Intuitively we would expect that this has to exceed 1 in order for a steady state to exist.

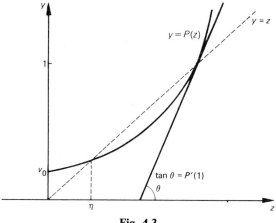

Fig. 4.3

Thus we obtain finally

$$u_k = (1 - \eta) \eta^k ; \tag{4.44}$$

$\beta = (1 - \eta)$ since $\sum_{n=0}^{\infty} u_k = 1$.

Thus in the case of negative exponential service the number of customers found in the system by an arrival has a geometric distribution [compare equation (4.44) with equation (2.25)].

$$u_0 = 1 - \eta \tag{4.45}$$

is the probability that the system is found (or left) empty.

Of course from equation (4.34) we see that

$$P(z) = \sum_{i=0}^{\infty} v_i z^i = A^*[\mu(1 - z)] \tag{4.46}$$

where $A^*(s) = \int_0^{\infty} e^{-st} a(t) \, dt$ is the Laplace transform of $a(t)$. This result should be compared with equation (4.23).

Consider the time X spent in the queue by an arrival in the steady-state situation.

$$\Pr(X = 0) = u_0 = 1 - \eta. \tag{4.47}$$

When X is non-zero it has a continuous distribution with probability density function $\phi(x)$ and the argument of Section 2.3 can be used to show that

$$\phi(x) = \sum_{j=1}^{\infty} u_j \frac{(\mu x)^{j-1} e^{-\mu x}}{(j-1)!} \mu$$

$$= \sum_{j=1}^{\infty} \frac{(1-\eta) \eta^j (\mu x)^{j-1} e^{-\mu x} \mu}{(j-1)!}$$

$$= \mu\eta(1-\eta) e^{-\mu x(1-\eta)}; \quad x \geqslant 0. \tag{4.48}$$

It is left as an exercise for the reader to follow through the analysis [similar to that which established equations (2.36) and (2.37) from equations (2.32) and (2.35)] to show that the time spent in the system is a random variable Y with probability density function

$$\psi(y) = \mu(1-\eta) e^{-\mu(1-\eta)y}; \quad y \geqslant 0. \tag{4.49}$$

Thus the time spent in the system has a negative exponential distribution when the service time has a negative exponential distribution.

All the results derived hinge on our knowing the value of η. In general a numerical procedure (Newton's Method for example) will have to be employed in order to solve the equation, (to find the root <1).

$$\eta = P(\eta).$$

Exercises 4

1   The results (4.14) and (4.15) give the average number of customers in the system in the case of negative exponential service and constant service (with the same mean) for the M/G/1 system. Show that for values of ρ near to 1 the effect of reducing the variance to zero is to halve (approximately) the average number in the system in the two cases.

2   One inspector is responsible for checking and correcting assemblies brought to him by a group of men. Observations show that the men bring their work to the inspector at an average rate of 12 per hour, their arrivals being approximately random. The checking and correcting can be thought of as two phases in the total service, the times being correlated with coefficient of correlation 0.8. The checking time is normally distributed with mean 1 minute and standard deviation $\frac{1}{2}$ minute. The correcting time is normally distributed with mean 3 minutes and standard deviation 1 minute.

Find the proportion of time for which the inspector is free, the mean number of men in the queue, and the mean waiting time spent in the queue.

3   If the arrivals in a queue occur randomly at rate λ and service times are exponentially distributed with mean $1/\mu$ show that the probability of r arrivals during a single service time is

$$p_r = \left(\frac{\lambda}{\lambda + \mu}\right)^r \left(\frac{\mu}{\lambda + \mu}\right), \quad r = 0, 1, 2, \ldots$$

and that the probability generating function of this distribution is

$$P(z) = \sum_{r=0}^{\infty} p_r z^r = \frac{\mu}{\mu + \lambda(1 - z)}.$$

When the number in the system is stationary let the probability that the number in the system is q at the end of a servicing be denoted by π_q and the probability generating function of this distribution by

$$\pi(z) = \sum_{q=0}^{\infty} \pi_q z^q.$$

By showing that the probability generating function of $q - U(q)$ is

$$\frac{\pi(z) - \pi_0(1 - z)}{z}$$

prove that

$$\pi(z) = \frac{\pi_0(1 - z) P(z)}{P(z) - z}.$$

Hence, using the fact that $\pi_0 = 1 - \dfrac{\lambda}{\mu}$, show that

$$\pi_q = \left(\frac{\lambda}{\mu}\right)^q \left(1 - \frac{\lambda}{\mu}\right).$$

4   Emergency cases to a casualty unit in a hospital arrive randomly at an average rate of one every five hours. Treatment to such patients consists of two phases which are uncorrelated;

   (i) examination, X-ray and diagnosis which takes 15 minutes,
   (ii) time in the operating theatre which has mean 1 hour and standard deviation $\frac{1}{2}$
        hour.

Although in practice critical cases would be given immediate priority, it is felt that even if this were not so, patients should not have to wait more than 15 minutes for attention.

By considering the mean of the waiting time distribution say whether you think this is likely to be so.

5   In the case of a queue with random arrivals at rate λ and service time distribution with probability density function

$$b(t) = \frac{k\mu(k\mu t)^{k-1} e^{-k\mu t}}{(k - 1)!}; \quad t \geqslant 0$$

show that

(i) $L_q = \dfrac{k+1}{2k} \cdot \dfrac{\lambda^2}{\mu(\mu - \lambda)}$

(ii) $L = \dfrac{\lambda}{\mu} + \dfrac{k+1}{2k} \cdot \dfrac{\lambda^2}{\mu(\mu - \lambda)}$

(iii) $W_q = \dfrac{k+1}{2k} \cdot \dfrac{\lambda}{\mu(\mu - \lambda)}$

(iv) $W = \dfrac{k+1}{2k} \cdot \dfrac{\lambda}{\mu(\mu - \lambda)} + \dfrac{1}{\mu}$.

Note the validity of $L = \lambda W$, $L_q = \lambda W_q$ for the $\text{M}/\text{E}_k/1$ system.

6 By letting $k \to \infty$ in Question 5 find corresponding results in the case of constant service time.

7 An aeroplane takes almost exactly 4 minutes to land after it has been given the landing signal by flight control. If aeroplanes arrive at random at an average rate of 8 per hour, how long can an aeroplane expect to have to circle the airport before getting the signal to land?

8 For a single-server queue, customers arrive at random at an average rate λ and the length of service is b ($\lambda b < 1$). Find the Laplace Transform of the service time distribution. Deduce the Laplace Transform of the time spent in the queue. Deduce the mean and variance of this time.

9 Consider the M/D/1 system in which arrivals occur at random at an average rate λ and service time is a constant of duration b and $(\rho =)\lambda b < 1$.
   Use the formulae (4.21) and (4.23) to write down an expression for the generating function for the π_k, where π_k is the probability that a departing customer leaves k customers in the system. Show that in this case

$$Q(z) = \frac{(1 - \rho)(1 - z)}{1 - z\,e^{\rho(1 - z)}}.$$

Show that $Q(1) = 1$ (L'Hopital's Rule). By considering $\dfrac{dQ}{dz}\Big|_{z=1}$ evaluate the mean of the number left in the system at a moment of departure.

10 For the M/G/1 system arrivals occur at random at an average rate λ and service time has probability density function

$$b(t) = \mu^2\, t\, e^{-\mu t}; \quad t \geqslant 0.$$

   Find the condition for a steady-state solution and find the generating function for the distribution of the number left behind by a departing customer. Find also the average number left in the system by a departing customer.

11   For the G/M/1 system show that the average number of customers found in the system by an arrival is

$$L = \frac{\eta}{1 - \eta}$$

where η is the smallest root ($\eta < 1$) of the equation

$$z = A^*[\lambda(1 - z)]$$

where $A^*(s)$ is the Laplace Transform of the inter-arrival time distribution. Show that L is an increasing function of η.

12   Show that for the system of Question 11, the mean queueing time of an arrival is $\frac{\eta}{\mu(1 - \eta)}$ and deduce the mean time spent in the system is $\frac{1}{\mu(1 - \eta)}$.

13   Use the argument employed to derive equations (2.36) and (2.37) from equations (2.32) and (2.35) to show that the time spent in the system for the G/M/1 queue has probability density function

$$\psi(y) = \mu(1 - \eta)\, y\, e^{-\mu(1 - \eta)y}; \quad y \geqslant 0.$$

Deduce that the mean time in the system is $\frac{1}{\mu(1 - \eta)}$.

14   Apply the method of Section 4.3 to the M/M/1 system. Show that $P(z)$ as given by equation (4.46) takes the form

$$P(z) = \frac{\lambda}{\lambda + \mu(1 - z)}.$$

Show that the condition $P'(1) > 1$ (equation (4.43)) is equivalent to $(\lambda/\mu) < 1$. In that case show that the smallest root of the equation

$$z = P(z)$$

is $z = (\lambda/\mu)(= \eta)$ as we would expect. Thus the distribution of the number found by an arriving customer is the same as the distribution for the number in the system at an arbitrary moment for this system.

15   Compare the D/M/1 system with the M/M/1 system. For the latter the average number in the system is $\rho/(1 - \rho)$. For the former show that if the inter-arrival time has the constant value $1/\lambda$ then η is the smallest solution of the equation

$$z = e^{-\frac{\mu}{\lambda}(1 - z)}.$$

Now in the light of Question 11 if $\eta < \lambda/\mu$ the average number in the system and indeed the mean queueing time will be reduced as compared with the M/M/1 system with the same arrival rate. Thus an appointments system with the same mean arrival rate would be preferable.

Try to construct a proof that if $\rho < 1$ the smallest root of the equation

$$z = e^{-\frac{1}{\rho}(1-z)}$$

is less than ρ.

16   Customers to a single-server queue arrive at random at an average rate of 4 per hour. Service time has a negative exponential distribution with mean 12 minutes. Show that $\rho = 0.8$ and that the average number of customers in the system is 4 and the mean queueing time for a customer is 48 minutes.

Suppose an appointments system is organised so that customers arrive at 15 minute intervals. Show that

$$\eta \simeq 0.62863 \quad (< \rho \text{ of course}).$$

Deduce that the average number of customers in the system when a customer arrives is 1.693 and the mean waiting time in the queue is 20.31 minutes.

What is the probability that a customer has to wait in the case of (i) random arrivals, (ii) regular arrivals?

5
The Machine Interference Problem

5.1 The Practical Situation

The following practical situation, illustrated in Fig. 5.1, provides the motivation for much of the discussion which follows. An operative is in charge of a number of identical machines which break down from time to time. When a machine stops the operative repairs it and sets it running again. This repair will take a finite time and during this time a second (or third) machine might break down, and this will have to remain stopped until the operative is free to attend to it. Thus production will be lost, and it is in order to be able to predict this loss that various mathematical models of this system have been proposed.

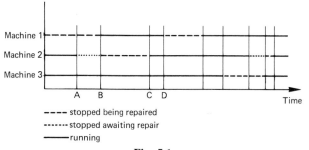

---- stopped being repaired
······ stopped awaiting repair
——— running

Fig. 5.1

In Fig. 5.1, the situation in which the operative has charge of three machines, is illustrated. As we start to observe the system the operative is repairing the first machine. At time A the second machine stops and has to wait stopped until time B when the repair on the first machine is completed. The operative then repairs machine 2, completing this repair at time C. All the machines then run until time D when the first machine stops again. The operative can start on this repair immediately. Variations on this type of pattern will describe the behaviour of the system over time. Production is lost whenever a machine is stopped, whether it is being repaired or waiting to be repaired. The term machine interference is generally reserved for the loss of production due to a machine having to wait for repair.

Two quantities of fundamental importance in discussing this problem are the Operative Utilisation (the proportion of time that the operative is working on repairs), and the Machine Efficiency (the ratio of the total production achieved to that which would have occurred had no stoppages taken place). The latter quantity is often expressed as a percentage. Thus suppose the operative looks after 10 machines and that during an 8 hour shift he spends 7 hours on repairs and that a total of 60 machine hours of production are obtained. The operative utilisation would be

$$P = \frac{7}{8} \text{ or } 87.5\%.$$

The machine efficiency would be

$$E = \frac{60}{8 \times 10} = \frac{3}{4} \text{ or } 75\%.$$

An alternative to the efficiency is to consider the average number of machines running, i.e. the number of machines which running for the whole time would have achieved the production actually obtained. For the example just cited this would be 7.5 (out of the 10).

In general, if the operative looks after N machines and we consider the system over a long time T hours, during which time the operative actually works on repairs for T_0 hours, and a total of T_r running hours are achieved, then

$$\text{Operative Utilisation} = P = T_0/T, \qquad (5.1)$$

$$\text{Efficiency} = E = T_r/NT. \qquad (5.2)$$

There is a simple relationship between these two quantities. If the mean number of stops per unit running time per machine is λ, and the mean repair time is c, then in time T, there will be a total of λT_r stops (asymptotically) and it will take a time $\lambda T_r c$ to repair these stops.

$$T_0 = \lambda T_r c = \rho T_r \qquad (5.3)$$

where $\rho = \lambda c$.

$$\therefore \quad \text{Operative Utilisation} = P = \frac{\rho T_r}{T} = N\rho E. \qquad (5.4)$$

$$\therefore \quad E = \frac{P}{N\rho}. \qquad (5.5)$$

If $N = 1$ the operative looks after just one machine. The operative utilisation will then be $\rho/(1 + \rho)$, since each hour of running will require ρ hours of repair. The efficiency is just $1/(1 + \rho)$. We have already investigated this problem in Section 2.1 in the case of random breakdowns with negative exponential repair times $\left(c = \frac{1}{\mu} \text{ and } \rho = \frac{\lambda}{\mu} \right)$. Questions 2, 3 and 4 of Exercises 2 also considered the problem and indeed we have just answered Question 2, for the efficiency can be interpreted as the proportion of time for which the machine is running.

It is also possible to deal with the case in which $N \to \infty$, i.e. the operative has charge of a very large number of machines. In this situation the operative utilisation P will be 1. He will be working for the whole time. Thus from equation (5.5)

$$E \to \frac{1}{N\rho}.$$

It is perhaps more informative to look at the average number of machines running in this case.

This is given by

$$NE \to \frac{1}{\rho}. \tag{5.6}$$

Thus there is an upper limit to the average number of machines running which approaches $1/\rho$, no matter how many machines are assigned to the operative.

For other values of N, apart from the extremes of 1 and $N \to \infty$, we shall need to make a more detailed study of the nature of the breakdowns, and the distribution of repair times before we can construct a model for the problem.

5.2 The M/M/1 Machine Interference Model

In this section we develop the model considered by Benson and Cox in their paper published in the *Journal of the Royal Statistical Society* in 1951. Thus we assume that the operative has charge of N identical machines which each break down independently at random at an average rate λ in running time. Thus for each machine the running time (the time between it being set running and next breaking down) has a negative exponential distribution with mean $1/\lambda$. It is further assumed that repair times also have a negative exponential distribution with mean $1/\mu$.

This model thus gives rise to a particular case of the birth–death equations. We define $p_n(t)$ to be the probability that n machines (out of the N machines) are stopped at time t. Then $N - n$ of the machines will be running so that the 'arrival rate' is

$$\lambda_n = \lambda(N - n); \quad n = 0, 1, 2, \ldots, N.$$

Since there is one operative, the service (repair) rate is

$$\mu_n = \mu \quad \text{for all values of } n.$$

Thus in line with equation (3.6), for the *steady-state* situation,

$$p_1 = N \frac{\lambda}{\mu} p_0, \quad p_2 = N(N-1)\left(\frac{\lambda}{\mu}\right)^2 p_0,$$

$$p_3 = N(N-1)(N-2)\left(\frac{\lambda}{\mu}\right)^3 p_0 \text{ etc.,}$$

$$p_N = N!\left(\frac{\lambda}{\mu}\right)^N p_0.$$

Thus

$$p_n = \frac{N!}{(N-n)!}\left(\frac{\lambda}{\mu}\right)^n p_0, \quad n = 0, 1, 2, \ldots, N. \tag{5.7}$$

To find p_0 we use the condition

$$\sum_{n=0}^{N} p_n = 1$$

which leads to

$$p_0 = 1/\{1 + N\rho + N(N-1)\rho^2 + \cdots + N!\,\rho^N\} \qquad (5.8)$$

where $\rho = \dfrac{\lambda}{\mu}$.

It is convenient to denote the denominator in equation (5.8) by

$$F(N, \rho) = 1 + N\rho + N(N-1)\rho^2 + N(N-1)(N-2)\rho^3 + \cdots + N!\,\rho^N. \quad (5.9)$$

We may interpret p_0 as the proportion of time for which all the machines are running. The operative utilisation will be simply $1 - p_0$. Then from equation (5.5) with P replaced by $1 - p_0$ we obtain for the machine efficiency

$$E = \frac{(1 - p_0)}{N\rho},$$

$$\therefore \quad E = \frac{1}{N\rho} \cdot \frac{F(N, \rho) - 1}{F(N, \rho)}. \qquad (5.10)$$

However we note that

$$F(N, \rho) = 1 + N\rho[1 + (N-1)\rho + (N-1)(N-2)\rho^2 + \cdots (N-1)!\,\rho^{N-1}]$$

$$\therefore \quad F(N, \rho) = 1 + N\rho F(N-1, \rho). \qquad (5.11)$$

We have of course $\qquad\qquad F(0, \rho) = 1. \qquad\qquad\qquad\qquad (5.12)$

Thus we may write equation (5.10) as

$$E = \frac{F(N-1, \rho)}{F(N, \rho)}. \qquad (5.13)$$

For a given value of ρ we may use equations (5.11) and (5.12) to calculate the polynomials $F(M, \rho)$ for $M = 0, 1, 2, \ldots, N$ and then use equation (5.13) to calculate the efficiency. The program which follows does this and was used to construct Table 5.1. For different values of ρ (R in the program), the values of $F(M, \rho)$ are calculated

```
LIST
  10 PRINT"MACHINE INTERFERENCE,MACHINE EFFICIENCY (%),EXPONENTIAL REPAIRS"
  20 DIM F(80):PRINT""
  30 READ N:REM N IS LARGEST NUMBER OF MACHINES TO BE CONSIDERED.
  40 PRINT"                      NUMBER OF MACHINES"
  50 @%=&000003:PRINT"   R     ";
  60 FOR I=1 TO N:PRINT I;"   ";:NEXT I :PRINT""
  70 @%=&20206
  80 FOR PP=2 TO 40 STEP 2
  90 R=PP/100:PRINT R;
 100 F(0)-1
 110 FOR M-1 TO N
 120 F(M)=1+M*R*F(M-1)
 130 NEXT M
 210 FOR M=1 TO N
 220 EFF=100*F(M-1)/F(M)
 230 PRINT EFF;
 240 NEXT M
 250 PRINT""
 260 NEXT PP
 280 DATA 12
 300 END
```

at lines 1∅∅–13∅. The efficiency is calculated at line 22∅. Line 2∅ allows us to deal with up to 8∅ machines but could clearly be modified. The format statements at lines 5∅ and 7∅ allow the results to be presented in compact form. In Table 5.2 the average number of machines running ($N \times E$) is tabulated. The limiting values for large N as given by equation (5.6) are readily apparent in the bottom right hand corner of the table. Table 5.3 shows the Operative Utilisation as a percentage. In general high values of the operative utilisation will mean low values for the efficiency and vice versa and this is easily seen to be the case. The reader is invited to extend the tables.

Table 5.1

```
>RUN
MACHINE INTERFERENCE,MACHINE EFFICIENCY (%),EXPONENTIAL REPAIRS

                              NUMBER OF MACHINES
     R     1     2     3     4     5     6     7     8     9    10    11    12
   0.02 98.04 98.00 97.96 97.92 97.88 97.84 97.79 97.74 97.69 97.64 97.59 97.53
   0.04 96.15 96.01 95.86 95.70 95.52 95.33 95.13 94.91 94.67 94.41 94.13 93.82
   0.06 94.34 94.04 93.71 93.34 92.94 92.49 91.99 91.44 90.82 90.12 89.35 88.47
   0.08 92.59 92.09 91.52 90.88 90.16 89.34 88.40 87.34 86.13 84.76 83.20 81.44
   0.10 90.91 90.16 89.31 88.33 87.21 85.91 84.42 82.71 80.75 78.54 76.07 73.36
   0.12 89.29 88.27 87.10 85.73 84.14 82.29 80.16 77.72 74.97 71.93 68.64 65.19
   0.14 87.72 86.42 84.89 83.09 80.99 78.55 75.75 72.59 69.11 65.39 61.56 57.74
   0.16 86.21 84.60 82.69 80.45 77.81 74.77 71.31 67.51 63.46 59.30 55.21 51.33
   0.18 84.75 82.82 80.52 77.81 74.64 71.01 66.98 62.65 58.21 53.85 49.73 45.97
   0.20 83.33 81.08 78.39 75.21 71.51 67.35 62.82 58.12 53.47 49.08 45.08 41.52
   0.22 81.97 79.39 76.29 72.65 68.46 63.82 58.91 53.97 49.26 44.95 41.13 37.81
   0.24 80.65 77.73 74.25 70.15 65.51 60.46 55.27 50.21 45.54 41.38 37.78 34.69
   0.26 79.37 76.12 72.25 67.73 62.67 57.30 51.92 46.84 42.27 38.30 34.91 32.04
   0.28 78.12 74.56 70.30 65.38 59.96 54.33 48.85 43.81 39.39 35.62 32.44 29.75
   0.30 76.92 73.03 68.41 63.12 57.39 51.57 46.05 41.10 36.85 33.28 30.29 27.77
   0.32 75.76 71.55 66.58 60.94 54.95 49.00 43.49 38.67 34.60 31.22 28.40 26.04
   0.34 74.63 70.11 64.80 58.86 52.64 46.62 41.17 36.49 32.60 29.39 26.73 24.51
   0.36 73.53 68.71 63.08 56.86 50.47 44.42 39.05 34.53 30.81 27.76 25.25 23.15
   0.38 72.46 67.36 61.42 54.95 48.43 42.38 37.12 32.76 29.20 26.31 23.92 21.93
   0.40 71.43 66.04 59.82 53.13 46.51 40.49 35.36 31.15 27.75 24.99 22.73 20.83
```

Table 5.2

```
>RUN
MACHINE INTERFERENCE,AVERAGE NUMBER RUNNING, EXPONENTIAL REPAIRS

                              NUMBER OF MACHINES
     R     2     4     6     8    10    12    14    16    18    20    22    24
   0.01  1.98  3.96  5.94  7.92  9.89 11.87 13.84 15.81 17.79 19.76 21.73 23.69
   0.02  1.96  3.92  5.87  7.82  9.76 11.70 13.64 15.56 17.48 19.40 21.30 23.18
   0.03  1.94  3.87  5.80  7.71  9.61 11.50 13.37 15.22 17.05 18.84 20.59 22.30
   0.04  1.92  3.83  5.72  7.59  9.44 11.26 13.04 14.76 16.43 18.00 19.47 20.80
   0.05  1.90  3.78  5.64  7.46  9.24 10.96 12.61 14.16 15.57 16.82 17.87 18.68
   0.06  1.88  3.73  5.55  7.32  9.01 10.62 12.09 13.40 14.50 15.36 15.96 16.33
   0.07  1.86  3.68  5.46  7.16  8.76 10.22 11.49 12.53 13.30 13.80 14.08 14.21
   0.08  1.84  3.64  5.36  6.99  8.48  9.77 10.82 11.59 12.07 12.33 12.44 12.48
   0.09  1.82  3.58  5.26  6.81  8.17  9.30 10.13 10.66 10.93 11.05 11.10 11.11
   0.10  1.80  3.53  5.15  6.62  7.85  8.80  9.43  9.78  9.93  9.98 10.00 10.00
   0.11  1.78  3.48  5.05  6.42  7.53  8.31  8.77  8.98  9.06  9.08  9.09  9.09
   0.12  1.77  3.43  4.94  6.22  7.19  7.82  8.15  8.28  8.32  8.33  8.33  8.33
   0.13  1.75  3.38  4.83  6.01  6.86  7.36  7.59  7.67  7.69  7.69  7.69  7.69
   0.14  1.73  3.32  4.71  5.81  6.54  6.93  7.08  7.13  7.14  7.14  7.14  7.14
   0.15  1.71  3.27  4.60  5.60  6.23  6.53  6.63  6.66  6.67  6.67  6.67  6.67
   0.16  1.69  3.22  4.49  5.40  5.93  6.16  6.23  6.25  6.25  6.25  6.25  6.25
   0.17  1.67  3.17  4.37  5.20  5.65  5.82  5.87  5.88  5.88  5.88  5.88  5.88
   0.18  1.66  3.11  4.26  5.01  5.39  5.52  5.55  5.55  5.56  5.56  5.56  5.56
   0.19  1.64  3.06  4.15  4.83  5.14  5.24  5.26  5.26  5.26  5.26  5.26  5.26
   0.20  1.62  3.01  4.04  4.65  4.91  4.98  5.00  5.00  5.00  5.00  5.00  5.00
```

Table 5.3

```
>RUN
MACHINE INTERFERENCE,EXPONENTIAL REPAIRS,OPERATIVE UTILISATION(%)

                        NUMBER OF MACHINES
   R     2     4     6     8    10    12    14    16    18    20    22    24
0.01   1.98  3.96  5.94  7.92  9.89 11.87 13.84 15.81 17.79 19.76 21.73 23.69
0.02   3.92  7.83 11.74 15.64 19.53 23.41 27.28 31.13 34.97 38.79 42.59 46.37
0.03   5.82 11.62 17.39 23.14 28.84 34.51 40.12 45.67 51.15 56.52 61.78 66.89
0.04   7.68 15.31 22.88 30.37 37.76 45.04 52.15 59.06 65.70 72.01 77.88 83.20
0.05   9.50 18.91 28.19 37.30 46.20 54.82 63.06 70.80 77.87 84.11 89.33 93.39
0.06  11.28 22.40 33.30 43.89 54.07 63.70 72.56 80.43 87.03 92.15 95.75 97.97
0.07  13.03 25.79 38.20 50.10 61.30 71.52 80.44 87.70 93.08 96.59 98.55 99.47
0.08  14.73 29.08 42.88 55.90 67.80 78.18 86.59 92.72 96.59 98.65 99.55 99.87
0.09  16.40 32.26 47.33 61.26 73.56 83.67 91.14 95.90 98.41 99.49 99.86 99.97
0.10  18.03 35.33 51.55 66.17 78.54 88.03 94.32 97.77 99.29 99.81 99.96 99.99
```

The derivation of the results obtained in this section follows the work of Benson and Cox (1951). It is interesting to note that Ashcroft (1950) had solved the problem for any distribution of the repair time. His argument was based on obtaining the operative utilisation by computing the average duration of the periods for which the operative was respectively idle and busy. We shall not repeat his arguments here although the reader is urged to consult the reference given. The expression for the average number of machines running in the cases of exponentially distributed repair times and constant repair time (of length $1/\mu$ to have the same mean as before) is as follows:

$$\text{Average Number of Machines Running} = \frac{NY_N}{1 + N\rho Y_N} \qquad (5.14)$$

where

$$Y_N = 1 + (N-1)\,\rho + (N-1)(N-2)\,\rho^2 + \cdots + (N-1)!\,\rho^{N-1}, \qquad (5.15)$$

for negative exponential repair time with mean $\frac{\lambda}{\mu}\left(\rho = \frac{\lambda}{\mu}\right)$, and

$$Y_N = 1 + \binom{N-1}{1}(e^\rho - 1) + \binom{N-1}{2}(e^\rho - 1)(e^{2\rho} - 1)\cdots$$

$$+ \binom{N-1}{N-1}(e^\rho - 1)(e^{2\rho} - 1)\cdots(e^{(N-1)\rho} - 1) \qquad (5.16)$$

for constant repair time of duration $1/\mu$. It is easy to see that equations (5.14) and (5.15) give a result equivalent to equation (5.13).

It is left as an exercise for readers to compute the equivalent of Table 5.2 (using equations (5.14) and (5.16)) in the case of constant repairs. When this is done it will be noted that for the same values of N and ρ, constant repairs give slightly higher values for the average number of machines running. The differences are quite small but are consistent. We can also use Ashcroft's method to investigate other repair time distributions but having a common mean $1/\mu$. Constant repair times give the highest efficiency in line with the principle that reducing the variance of the (service) repair time will lead to less queueing. However, the results are not too dependent on the shape of the distribution although they are very dependent on the mean (via ρ).

It has already been noted that in general low operative utilisation will go hand in hand with high efficiency and vice versa. This raises the problem of the optimum number of machines that the operative should look after. Various cost criteria could be used. If an operative costs $£C_0$ per hour and a machine $£C_m$ per hour and N machines are allocated to the operative, the cost per machine-running hour of production is

$$C = \frac{C_0 + NC_m}{NE(\rho, N)} \tag{5.17}$$

where E, the efficiency, is of course a function of ρ and N.

Thus in order to minimise C we give the operative N machines rather than $(N-1)$ if

$$\frac{C_0 + NC_m}{NE(\rho, N)} < \frac{C_0 + (N-1)\,C_m}{(N-1)\,E(\rho, N-1)}.$$

This is equivalent (after a little algebra) to

$$\frac{C_0}{C_m} > \frac{N(N-1)[E(\rho, N-1) - E(\rho, N)]}{NE(\rho, N) - (N-1)\,E(\rho, N-1)} = f_N(\rho). \tag{5.18}$$

Similarly we can establish that we give the operative N machines rather than $N-1$ or $N+1$ if

$$f_N(\rho) < \frac{C_0}{C_m} < f_{N+1}(\rho), \tag{5.19}$$

where

$$f_N(\rho) = \frac{N(N-1)[E(\rho, N-1) - E(\rho, N)]}{NE(\rho, N) - (N-1)\,E(\rho, N-1)}. \tag{5.20}$$

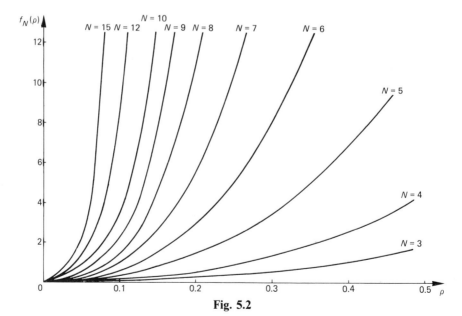

Fig. 5.2

Fig. 5.2 shows the graphs of $f_N(\rho)$ against ρ for various values of N. From such a chart it is a simple matter for a work study officer to determine the optimal number of machines to allocate, given values for ρ, C_0 and C_m. One locates the point $\left(\rho, \dfrac{C_0}{C_m}\right)$ on the chart. If this lies between $f_m(\rho)$ and $f_{m+1}(\rho)$ the optimal value is m.

5.3 The Case of Several Operatives

We can treat the case of m operatives looking after N machines by a similar method if we assume random breakdowns and negative exponential repairs, the $M/M/m$ machine interference problem. The case of other repair time distributions is much more difficult. The $M/D/2$ model has been treated by Mack and Stoodley (1968) and more recently the $M/E_k/r$ model has been discussed by Maritas and Xirokostas. Bunday and Scraton have shown that as far as the steady-state distribution of the number of stopped machines is concerned the $G/M/r$ and $M/M/r$ models have the same solution. Thus the same efficiency results in the case of exponential repairs whatever the distribution of running times. It is only dependent on the average breakdown rate (λ). Thus the $M/M/r$ machine interference model is a useful one to solve.

Its solution can be obtained as a special case of the birth–death equations. The *steady-state* probability p_n that n machines are stopped is a solution of the birth–death equations with

$$\left.\begin{aligned}
\lambda_n &= \lambda(N-n), & n &\leqslant N \\
&= 0 & n &> N \\
\mu_n &= n\mu, & n &\leqslant m \\
&= m\mu & n &> m
\end{aligned}\right\} \tag{5.21}$$

This leads to

$$\begin{aligned}
p_n &= \binom{N}{n} \rho^n p_0 & n &< m, \\[2mm]
p_n &= \frac{N!\,\rho^n}{(N-n)!\,m!\,m^{n-m}} p_0 & n &\geqslant m,
\end{aligned} \tag{5.22}$$

where $\rho = \dfrac{\lambda}{\mu}$.

Since $\sum_{n=0}^{N} p_n = 1$ we readily obtain

$$\begin{aligned}
\frac{1}{p_0} &= \sum_{n=0}^{m-1} \binom{N}{n} \rho^n + \sum_{n=m}^{N} \frac{N!\,\rho^n}{(N-n)!\,m!\,m^{n-m}} \\[2mm]
&= \sum_{n=0}^{m-1} \binom{N}{n} \rho^n + \frac{N!}{m!(N-m)!} \rho^m \sum_{r=0}^{N-m} \frac{(N-m)!}{(N-m-r)!} \left(\frac{\rho}{m}\right)^r \\[2mm]
&= \sum_{n=0}^{m-1} \binom{N}{n} \rho^n + \binom{N}{m} \rho^m F\left(N-m, \frac{\rho}{m}\right) \\[2mm]
&= \phi(N, m, \rho) \quad \text{say}
\end{aligned} \tag{5.23}$$

where we have used the polynomial $F(N, \rho)$ as defined by equation (5.9).

We can establish a recurrence for $\phi(N, m, \rho)$ which helps in its computation.

$$\phi(N, m, \rho) = \sum_{n=0}^{m-1} \binom{N}{n} \rho^n + \binom{N}{m} \rho^m F\left(N - m, \frac{\rho}{m}\right)$$

$$= \sum_{n=0}^{m-1} \binom{N}{n} \rho^n + \binom{N}{m} \rho^m \left[1 + \frac{(N-m)}{m} \rho F\left(N - m - 1, \frac{\rho}{m}\right)\right]$$

$$= \sum_{n=0}^{m-1} \binom{N}{n} \rho^n + \binom{N}{m} \rho^m + \frac{N\rho}{m}\left[\binom{N-1}{m} \rho^m F\left(N - m - 1, \frac{\rho}{m}\right)\right]$$

$$= \sum_{n=0}^{m-1} \binom{N}{n} \rho^n + \binom{N}{m} \rho^m + \frac{N\rho}{m}\left[\phi(N - 1, m, \rho) - \sum_{n=0}^{m-1} \binom{N-1}{n} \rho^n\right]$$

$$= \frac{N\rho}{m} \phi(N - 1, m, \rho) + \sum_{n=1}^{m-1} \rho^n \left\{\binom{N}{n} - \frac{N}{m}\binom{N-1}{n-1}\right\}$$

$$+ \binom{N}{m} \rho^m + 1 - \frac{N}{m}\binom{N-1}{m-1} \rho^m$$

$$\therefore \quad \phi(N, m, \rho) = \frac{N\rho}{m} \phi(N - 1, m, \rho) + \sum_{n=0}^{m-1} \binom{N}{n} \rho^n \left(1 - \frac{n}{m}\right). \tag{5.24}$$

Further we have

$$\phi(m, m, \rho) = \sum_{n=0}^{m-1} \binom{m}{n} \rho^n + \rho^m F\left(0, \frac{\rho}{m}\right) = (1 + \rho)^m. \tag{5.25}$$

The average number of machines running is given by

$$\sum_{n=0}^{N} (N - n) p_n = \sum_{n=0}^{m-1} (N - n)\binom{N}{n} \rho^n p_0 + \sum_{n=m}^{N} \frac{(N-n)\, N!\, \rho^n}{(N-n)!\, m!\, m^{n-m}} p_0$$

$$= N \sum_{n=0}^{m-1} \binom{N-1}{n} \rho^n p_0 + N\binom{N-1}{m} \rho^m F\left(N - m - 1, \frac{\rho}{m}\right) p_0.$$

Thus the efficiency E is given by

$$E = \frac{\displaystyle\sum_{n=0}^{m-1} \binom{N-1}{n} \rho^n + \binom{N-1}{m} \rho^m F\left(N - 1 - m, \frac{\rho}{m}\right)}{\displaystyle\sum_{n=0}^{m-1} \binom{N}{n} \rho^n + \binom{N}{m} \rho^m F\left(N - m, \frac{\rho}{m}\right)}$$

$$\therefore \quad E = \frac{\phi(N - 1, m, \rho)}{\phi(N, m, \rho)}. \tag{5.26}$$

We can also consider the proportion of time for which each operative is working. If

n machines are stopped the probability that a particular operative is working is $\dfrac{n}{m}$ if $n \leqslant m$ or 1 if $n > m$.

Thus the proportion of time each operative is working is given by

$$P = \frac{1}{m} \sum_{n=1}^{m} n \binom{N}{n} \rho^n p_0 + \sum_{n=m+1}^{N} \frac{N!}{(N-n)!\,m!} \frac{\rho^n}{m^{n-m}} p_0$$

$$= \frac{N\rho}{m} p_0 \sum_{n=1}^{m-1} \binom{N-1}{n} \rho^n + \frac{N\rho}{m} p_0 \binom{N-1}{m} \rho^m F\left(N-m-1, \frac{\rho}{m}\right)$$

$$\therefore \quad P = \frac{N\rho}{m} E. \tag{5.27}$$

Equations (5.26) and (5.27) stand comparison with equations (5.13) and (5.5) respectively in the case of one operative.

Table 5.4

```
>RUN
MACHINE INTERFERENCE,N MACHINES-M OPERATIVES,EXPONENTIAL REPAIRS
            AVERAGE NUMBER OF MACHINES RUNNING

NUMBER OF OPERATIVES IS 1

                    NUMBER OF MACHINES
   R     2     4     6     8    10    12    14    16    18    20    22    24
 0.02  1.96  3.92  5.87  7.82  9.76 11.70 13.64 15.56 17.48 19.40 21.30 23.18
 0.04  1.92  3.83  5.72  7.59  9.44 11.26 13.04 14.76 16.43 18.00 19.47 20.80
 0.06  1.88  3.73  5.55  7.32  9.01 10.62 12.09 13.40 14.50 15.36 15.96 16.33
 0.08  1.84  3.64  5.36  6.99  8.48  9.77 10.82 11.59 12.07 12.33 12.44 12.48
 0.10  1.80  3.53  5.15  6.62  7.85  8.80  9.43  9.78  9.93  9.98 10.00 10.00
 0.12  1.77  3.43  4.94  6.22  7.19  7.82  8.15  8.28  8.32  8.33  8.33  8.33
 0.14  1.73  3.32  4.71  5.81  6.54  6.93  7.08  7.13  7.14  7.14  7.14  7.14
 0.16  1.69  3.22  4.49  5.40  5.93  6.16  6.23  6.25  6.25  6.25  6.25  6.25
 0.18  1.66  3.11  4.26  5.01  5.39  5.52  5.55  5.55  5.56  5.56  5.56  5.56
 0.20  1.62  3.01  4.04  4.65  4.91  4.98  5.00  5.00  5.00  5.00  5.00  5.00
NUMBER OF OPERATIVES IS 2

                    NUMBER OF MACHINES
   R     2     4     6     8    10    12    14    16    18    20    22    24
 0.02  1.96  3.92  5.88  7.84  9.80 11.76 13.72 15.68 17.64 19.59 21.55 23.51
 0.04  1.92  3.85  5.77  7.69  9.61 11.52 13.43 15.34 17.24 19.13 21.01 22.89
 0.06  1.89  3.77  5.66  7.53  9.40 11.26 13.11 14.94 16.74 18.52 20.26 21.96
 0.08  1.85  3.70  5.54  7.38  9.19 10.98 12.73 14.45 16.10 17.68 19.16 20.51
 0.10  1.82  3.63  5.43  7.21  8.96 10.66 12.30 13.84 15.27 16.55 17.63 18.50
 0.12  1.79  3.56  5.32  7.05  8.72 10.31 11.79 13.12 14.26 15.17 15.83 16.25
 0.14  1.75  3.50  5.21  6.88  8.46  9.92 11.22 12.30 13.13 13.69 14.02 14.18
 0.16  1.72  3.43  5.10  6.70  8.18  9.50 10.60 11.42 11.97 12.28 12.42 12.48
 0.18  1.69  3.37  4.99  6.52  7.89  9.06  9.95 10.54 10.88 11.03 11.09 11.11
 0.20  1.67  3.31  4.88  6.34  7.60  8.60  9.30  9.71  9.90  9.97  9.99 10.00
NUMBER OF OPERATIVES IS 3

                    NUMBER OF MACHINES
   R     4     6     8    10    12    14    16    18    20    22    24    26
 0.02  3.92  5.88  7.84  9.80 11.76 13.73 15.69 17.65 19.61 21.57 23.53 25.49
 0.04  3.85  5.77  7.69  9.61 11.54 13.46 15.38 17.30 19.22 21.14 23.05 24.97
 0.06  3.77  5.66  7.55  9.43 11.32 13.20 15.07 16.95 18.82 20.68 22.53 24.38
 0.08  3.70  5.56  7.41  9.25 11.10 12.93 14.76 16.58 18.38 20.16 21.91 23.64
 0.10  3.64  5.45  7.27  9.08 10.88 12.66 14.43 16.17 17.87 19.53 21.13 22.66
 0.12  3.57  5.35  7.13  8.90 10.65 12.38 14.07 15.71 17.28 18.77 20.14 21.37
 0.14  3.51  5.26  7.00  8.73 10.42 12.08 13.67 15.19 16.59 17.85 18.93 19.80
 0.16  3.45  5.17  6.87  8.55 10.19 11.76 13.24 14.60 15.80 16.79 17.56 18.09
 0.18  3.39  5.08  6.74  8.37  9.94 11.42 12.77 13.95 14.92 15.65 16.14 16.42
 0.20  3.33  4.99  6.62  8.20  9.69 11.07 12.27 13.26 14.00 14.49 14.78 14.92
```

Table 5.4 (continued)

```
>RUN
MACHINE INTERFERENCE,N MACHINES-M OPERATIVES,EXPONENTIAL REPAIRS
          AVERAGE NUMBER OF MACHINES RUNNING

NUMBER OF OPERATIVES IS 4
```

NUMBER OF MACHINES

R	4	6	8	10	12	14	16	18	20	22	24	26
0.02	3.92	5.88	7.84	9.80	11.76	13.73	15.69	17.65	19.61	21.57	23.53	25.49
0.04	3.85	5.77	7.69	9.62	11.54	13.46	15.38	17.31	19.23	21.15	23.07	25.00
0.06	3.77	5.66	7.55	9.43	11.32	13.21	15.09	16.98	18.86	20.74	22.62	24.50
0.08	3.70	5.56	7.41	9.26	11.11	12.96	14.81	16.65	18.49	20.33	22.16	23.98
0.10	3.64	5.45	7.27	9.09	10.90	12.72	14.53	16.33	18.12	19.90	21.66	23.41
0.12	3.57	5.36	7.14	8.93	10.71	12.48	14.24	16.00	17.73	19.44	21.11	22.74
0.14	3.51	5.26	7.02	8.77	10.51	12.24	13.96	15.65	17.31	18.92	20.47	21.94
0.16	3.45	5.17	6.89	8.61	10.32	12.01	13.67	15.29	16.86	18.35	19.74	21.00
0.18	3.39	5.08	6.78	8.46	10.13	11.77	13.37	14.91	16.36	17.70	18.90	19.92
0.20	3.33	5.00	6.66	8.31	9.94	11.53	13.05	14.50	15.82	16.99	17.98	18.74

```
NUMBER OF OPERATIVES IS 5
```

NUMBER OF MACHINES

R	6	8	10	12	14	16	18	20	22	24	26	28
0.02	5.88	7.84	9.80	11.76	13.73	15.69	17.65	19.61	21.57	23.53	25.49	27.45
0.04	5.77	7.69	9.62	11.54	13.46	15.38	17.31	19.23	21.15	23.08	25.00	26.92
0.06	5.66	7.55	9.43	11.32	13.21	15.09	16.98	18.87	20.75	22.64	24.52	26.41
0.08	5.56	7.41	9.26	11.11	12.96	14.81	16.66	18.51	20.36	22.21	24.06	25.90
0.10	5.45	7.27	9.09	10.91	12.73	14.54	16.36	18.17	19.98	21.78	23.58	25.37
0.12	5.36	7.14	8.93	10.71	12.50	14.28	16.06	17.83	19.59	21.35	23.09	24.81
0.14	5.26	7.02	8.77	10.52	12.27	14.02	15.76	17.49	19.20	20.89	22.56	24.19
0.16	5.17	6.90	8.62	10.34	12.06	13.77	15.46	17.14	18.79	20.41	21.98	23.48
0.18	5.08	6.78	8.47	10.16	11.85	13.52	15.17	16.79	18.36	19.88	21.33	22.67
0.20	5.00	6.67	8.33	9.99	11.64	13.26	14.86	16.42	17.91	19.31	20.60	21.75

```
NUMBER OF OPERATIVES IS 6
```

NUMBER OF MACHINES

R	6	8	10	12	14	16	18	20	22	24	26	28
0.02	5.88	7.84	9.80	11.76	13.73	15.69	17.65	19.61	21.57	23.53	25.49	27.45
0.04	5.77	7.69	9.62	11.54	13.46	15.38	17.31	19.23	21.15	23.08	25.00	26.92
0.06	5.66	7.55	9.43	11.32	13.21	15.09	16.98	18.87	20.75	22.64	24.53	26.41
0.08	5.56	7.41	9.26	11.11	12.96	14.81	16.67	18.52	20.37	22.22	24.07	25.92
0.10	5.45	7.27	9.09	10.91	12.73	14.55	16.36	18.18	20.00	21.81	23.62	25.43
0.12	5.36	7.14	8.93	10.71	12.50	14.28	16.07	17.85	19.63	21.41	23.18	24.95
0.14	5.26	7.02	8.77	10.53	12.28	14.03	15.78	17.53	19.28	21.01	22.74	24.45
0.16	5.17	6.90	8.62	10.34	12.07	13.79	15.51	17.22	18.92	20.61	22.28	23.93
0.18	5.08	6.78	8.47	10.17	11.86	13.55	15.23	16.91	18.56	20.20	21.81	23.37
0.20	5.00	6.67	8.33	10.00	11.66	13.32	14.97	16.60	18.20	19.78	21.30	22.76

Table 5.4 shows the average number of machines running in the case of m (M) operatives looking after N machines for various values of ρ ($= \lambda/\mu$). We have of course made the assumption that breakdowns occur at random at rate λ for each machine and that repair times have a negative exponential distribution with mean $1/\mu$. The few cases in which the machine interference problem with several operatives, but not exponential repair times has been solved, suggest that the tables will give reasonable answers in situations where these assumptions are not fully justified. A more comprehensive set of tables are those calculated by Peck and Hazelwood. It is left as an exercise for the reader to compute and extend Table 5.4.

Example 1

A team of 3 operatives looks after 18 identical looms. Faults on the looms (mainly breaks in the weft yarn) occur at random in running time at an average rate of about 1

every 20 minutes. Repairs take about 2 minutes on average.
  Find the effective rate of production.

  This is a simple case where we can use the tables if we assume that the repair time
has an exponential distribution. The latter assumption is probably dubious. The
repair is a fairly routine matter so it is more likely to be constant. However, the M/D/r
machine interference problem has not been solved, unless our reader can provide such
a solution. Thus our table value will be only an approximation. With $M = 3$, $N = 18$
and $\rho(\equiv R) = \left(\dfrac{0.05}{0.50}\right) = 0.1$ the average number of machines running is 16.17.

  It is important to remember that the operatives work as a team. If we say allocate
machines 1 to 6 to the first operative, 7 to 12 to the second and machines 13 to 18 to the
third, then in the case $M = 1$, $N = 6$, $\rho = 0.1$, the average number of machines
running is 5.15.
  We note that $3 \times 5.15 = 15.45 < 16.17$.
  Thus team working is more effective. Of course it avoids the situation where an
operative is idle whilst another has machines waiting for attention.

Exercises 5

1 For the M/M/1 machine interference problem show that the steady-state
probability that n machines (out of N machines) are stopped is given by

$$p_n = \frac{N!}{(N-n)!}\, \rho^n p_0$$

where $p_0 = 1/(1 + N\rho + N(N-1)\,\rho^2 + \cdots + N!\,\rho^N)$.
  Write a BASIC program to evaluate p_n for various values of N and ρ.

2 Show that the average number of machines running for the above problem as
given by $\displaystyle\sum_{n=0}^{N} (N-n)\,p_n$ is in accord with NE as given by equation (5.13).

3 Use your program from Question 1 and the result of Question 2 to compute and
extend the results given in Tables 5.1, 5.2 and 5.3.

4 N machines, each liable to stop with a probability $\lambda\delta t + \mathrm{o}(\delta t)$ in running time δt,
are serviced by one operative. Repair times are exponentially distributed with
probability density function $\mu e^{-\mu t}$. Find expressions for $p_0, p_1, \ldots, p_n$ where p_n is the
steady-state probability that n machines are stopped at a random instant. Find also,
expressions for

  (a) the proportion of time spent by the operative in repairing machines,
  (b) the proportion of time that any single machine is running,
and show that
  (c) the proportion of the total time that a machine spends waiting for attention is

$$\frac{(N-1)\,\rho^2 + 2(N-1)(N-2)\,\rho^3 + \cdots + (N-1)(N-1)!\,\rho^N}{1 + N\rho + N(N-1)\,\rho^2 + \cdots + N!\,\rho^N},$$

where $\rho = \dfrac{\lambda}{\mu}$.

5   Use the result just obtained in Question 4 to compute a table of values, for various values of N and ρ, of the proportion of time that a machine spends waiting for attention.

Observations show that the mean repair time is 2 minutes and the mean continuous run for a single machine is 40 minutes. What is the maximum number of machines that can be allocated to one operative if a machine must not spend more than 1% of the total time waiting for attention?

6   There are n machines, each liable to stop with a probability $\lambda \, dt$ in a running time dt. Repairs all take the same time c. With one repairman show that, if x_n is his mean busy period, then

$$x_n = c + p_1 x_n + p_2(x_n + x_{n-1}) + \cdots + p_{n-1}(x_n + x_{n-1} + \cdots + x_3 + x_2)$$

where

$$p_r = \binom{n-1}{r}(1 - e^{-\lambda c})^r \, e^{-(n-1-r)\lambda c}.$$

If $n = 3$ show that $x_3 = ca(a^2 - a + 1)$, $a \equiv e^{\lambda c}$.

Find an expression for the efficiency (ratio of running to total time) of the machines.

7   Use the results (5.14) and (5.16) to compute Tables 5.2 and 5.3 in the case of constant repair times (of duration $1/\mu$). Question 6 above illustrates Ashcroft's method for the case of 3 machines.

8   Consult Ashcroft's paper and hence compute Tables 5.2 and 5.3 for a rectangular distribution of repair times. Let the repair time have mean $1/\mu$ and range $1/\mu$. The results should lie between those obtained for constant repair time and exponential repair time.

9 N machines, each liable to random breakdown at a rate λ per unit running time, are serviced by $M(\leqslant N)$ servers, repair times X being exponentially distributed with probability density

$$p(x) = \mu \, e^{-\mu x}; \quad x \geqslant 0.$$

Use the birth–death equations to find the probability that no machines are broken down at any instant. For the case $M = N$, find also the probabilities p_n ($n = 0, 1, \ldots, N$) that n machines are broken down and determine the mean value of n. Note in this last case the number of broken down machines has a binomial stationary distribution.

10   Write a BASIC program to compute and extend Table 5.4.

6
Simulation Models

6.1 Introduction

So far our models have been analytical. We have been able to represent the behaviour of our systems by sets of equations which give relationships between the variables which describe the systems. These equations have been capable of solution. In this way we have been able to predict quantities such as the mean waiting time. We have also been able to investigate the effect of changes in the system. Of course in some more complex systems, we might find that we can only obtain numerical solutions to our equations. In others it may be difficult or even impossible to make the system tractable. We cannot conveniently express the relationships which govern the system in a mathematical form.

Then, and perhaps only then, we should consider simulation as a means of analysing the system. In simulation we try to build a model that will act like the system so that the behaviour of the model will duplicate the behaviour of the system, at least as far as the properties which are of interest. We still have to model the system, pick out its salient features and be sure that our model will mimic these at least in a representative way. Our model will contain parameters such as the average arrival rate, the number of servers etc. By varying these and observing the way in which the model responds we hope to extrapolate to the system itself.

We shall need to generate values for the random variables that arise. We need to be able to obtain typical values for the inter-arrival times and service times. It is possible to obtain tables which list values from many of the common distributions. Using these, and sorting out the logical behaviour of the system as we progress, it is possible to work the simulation 'by hand'. There is no real difficulty, although the work is tedious, and the amount to be done in order to derive reasonable solutions is enormous. Thus we seek the help of the computer and this makes table-look-up methods unsuitable in general.

We shall of course only have space to consider the elementary aspects of this topic. Simulation has applications to many areas in Operational Research apart from queues. Thus we shall not discuss in any detail the many important variance-reduction techniques which can lead to dramatic improvements in the accuracy of the simulation, and in the amount of work necessary to carry out the simulation. Nor shall we consider the specialist simulation languages (e.g. SIMULA, GPSS, GASPIV) which simplify the coding of simulation models. Rather we shall confine ourself to a relatively crude approach using BASIC illustrated by some simple examples.

6.2 Generating the Random Variables

Random Digits

The generation of random digits is the base from which the generation of other random variables is derived. A sequence of random digits may be defined to be a sequence of digits (one of the values 0, 1, 2, . . ., 7, 8, 9) such that at any point in the sequence the next digit is equally likely to be any one of 0, 1, 2, . . ., 9.

$$\Pr(\text{Next digit} = r) = \frac{1}{10}; \quad r = 0, 1, 2, \ldots, 9.$$

We can generate such digits mechanically in a number of ways. Write the values 0, 1, . . ., 9 on ten identical discs. Mix the discs in a box and draw one at random. Note the value written. Replace the disc, thoroughly mix the discs and draw a second. Note the value. The sequence we obtain will be a sequence of random digits. A more convenient method may be to use a twenty-faced die as illustrated in Fig. 6.1(a). Each face on this regular icosahedron is a triangle, two are marked 0, two are marked 1, etc. When it is thrown at random the probability that any particular digit is uppermost is 1/10. Yet another alternative is to use a roulette wheel with a circular scale divided into ten equal portions (Fig. 6.1(b)). Each spin of the wheel will generate a random digit.

(a)   (b)

Fig. 6.1

None of the methods just described is suitable for use with a digital computer. Most of these contain a random number generator or to be more precise a pseudo-random number generator. These generate in a deterministic way a string of digits which to all intents and purposes have the properties of random digits. It is not necessary for the user to know precisely how the generator works. It can be treated as a black box. In many machines the statement

$$3\emptyset \ X = RND(1\emptyset\emptyset)$$

will generate a random integer (a pair of digits) in the range 00, 01, 02, . . ., 98, 99.

Many of these generators work using a multiplicative–congruential scheme to obtain the sequence $x_0, x_1, x_2, \ldots,$ of integers where

$$x_{n+1} = kx_n \bmod m \tag{6.1}$$

[x_{n+1} is the remainder when kx_n is divided by m].

For example if $k = 7$ and $m = 10$, with $x_0 = 7$ we obtain

$x_1 = 9$ ($7 \times 7 = 49$ leaves remainder 9 when divided by 10)

$x_2 = 3$ ($7 \times 9 = 63$,,   ,,   3 ,,   ,,   ,, ,,)

$x_3 = 1$ ($7 \times 3 = 21$,,   ,,   1 ,,   ,,   ,, ,,)

$x_4 = 7$ ($7 \times 1 = 7$,,   ,,   7 ,,   ,,   ,, ,,)

etc.

Of course this generator will just reproduce the cycle of length 4, 7931 7931 7931 over and over again. This is nothing like a sequence of random digits. However, if we take $k = 455\,470\,314$ and $m = 2^{31} - 1 = 2\,147\,483\,647$ then the cycles have length $2^{31} - 2$ and each integer in the range $1, \ldots, 2^{31} - 2$ appears just once in the cycle. The overall sequence has many of the properties of a sequence of random digits.

Uniformly Distributed Variables

A random variable U with probability density function

$$f(u) = 1, \quad 0 \leqslant u \leqslant 1$$
$$= 0, \quad \text{elsewhere} \tag{6.2}$$

and distribution function

$$F(u) = 0, \quad u < 0$$
$$= u, \quad 0 \leqslant u \leqslant 1 \tag{6.3}$$
$$= 1, \quad u > 1$$

is said to be uniformly distributed over the range $(0, 1)$.

A sequence of k random digits preceded by a decimal point will represent a value for such a variable to k decimal place accuracy. From the random digits 60973 we derive the value 0.60973. In many computers the statement

$$40 \quad U = RND(1)$$

will generate a uniform variable to the accuracy of the machine, often 9 or 10 decimal places.

The Distribution Function Method

If we know the distribution function $F(x)$ of a random variable X and we have a value u for a uniform variable U, then by solving the equation

$$F(x) = u \tag{6.4}$$

for x we can obtain a value for X. This is illustrated in Fig. 6.2.

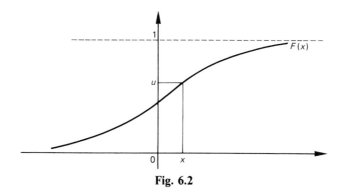

Fig. 6.2

$F(x)$ will assume values in the range (0, 1). If the value u is chosen at random in this range then since $F(x)$ is an increasing function of x, and if the value for X is derived from equation (6.4)

$$\Pr(X \leqslant x) = \Pr(U \leqslant u) = u = F(x).$$

Thus the values x are sample values from the required distribution.

We can use equation (6.4) to derive explicit formulae for some commonly occurring random variables. Thus if X has a negative exponential distribution with mean $1/\mu$, $F(x) = 1 - e^{-\mu x}$.

$$u = 1 - e^{-\mu x}$$

whence
$$x = -\frac{1}{\mu} \ln(1 - u) = -\frac{1}{\mu} \ln u', \qquad (6.5)$$

where u and $u' (= 1 - u)$ are values from a uniform distribution.

Example 1

Given a value u of a uniform random variable, show how to generate a random variable from (i) the distribution with probability density function

$$f(x) = 2x, \quad 0 \leqslant x \leqslant 1$$
$$= 0 \qquad \text{elsewhere,}$$

(ii) a Poisson distribution with mean 2.

(i) $F(x) = 0; \; x < 0$

$$F(x) = \int_0^x f(v) \, dv = x^2; \quad 0 \leqslant x \leqslant 1$$

$$= 1; \qquad\qquad x > 1.$$

Thus with $u = x^2$, $x = \sqrt{u}$ (Fig. 6.3(a)).

(ii)   We again use equation (6.4) but we have to give a numerical rather than a closed formula solution. We need to tabulate the distribution function involved. For the Poisson distribution with mean 2

$$\Pr(X = x) = \frac{e^{-2} 2^x}{x!}; \quad x = 0, 1, 2, \ldots$$

x	$Pr(X = x)$	$Pr(X \leqslant x) = F(x)$
0	0.1353	0.1353
1	0.2707	0.4060
2	0.2707	0.6767
3	0.1804	0.8571
4	0.0902	0.9473
5	0.0361	0.9834
6	0.0120	0.9954
7	0.0034	0.9988
8	0.0009	0.9997
9	0.0002	0.9999

Thus if $0 < u \leqslant 0.1353$, $x = 0$, if $0.1353 < u \leqslant 0.4060$, $x = 1$, etc. The distribution function is a step function (Fig. 6.3(b)).

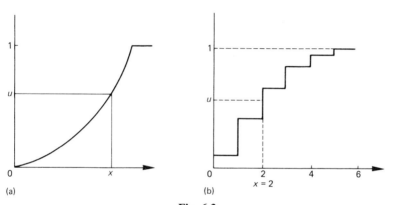

(a)   (b)

Fig. 6.3

Strictly speaking, we are not of course solving the equation

$$F(x) = u$$

in this case. Indeed since $F(x)$ only takes on certain values, the solution of the equation is only possible for those particular values of u. Rather for the discrete random variable X the simulated variate assumes the value x if the value of u is such that

$$F(x - 1) < u \leqslant F(x). \qquad (6.6)$$

Indeed even for continuous variables we might argue that for a given value u we generate the value x if

$$F(x - \delta x) < u \leqslant F(x). \qquad (6.7)$$

As $\delta x \to 0$, equation (6.7) is equivalent to equation (6.4).

The difficulty that arises in Example 1 (ii) is not uncommon. We cannot give a simple explicit form for $F(x)$ and we certainly cannot solve the equation

$$F(x) = u$$

except numerically.

Particular algorithms have been devised which allow the generation of random variables by the computer in such cases. We state without proof the Box–Müller method for the generation of a standard normal variate with mean 0 and standard deviation 1.

If U_1 and U_2 are independent uniform variables on $(0, 1)$ then

$$Z_1 = \sqrt{-2 \ln U_1} \cdot \cos(2\pi U_2)$$

and

$$Z_2 = \sqrt{-2 \ln U_2} \cdot \sin(2\pi U_2)$$

are independent $N(0, 1)$ variables.

From such a value Z we can derive a normal variable with mean μ and standard deviation σ as

$$\mu + \sigma Z.$$

Procedures to generate values from many other distributions are well known and are given in the references cited. The algorithm could be put into the form of a subroutine within the simulation program.

6.3   The Single-Server Queue

A computer program for the simulation of a single-server queue with a first come, first served discipline is presented in this section. Before discussing this in detail a few words about the general philosophy underlying such models are appropriate. We seek to simulate the system over a period of time. During this period certain events happen at certain times which bring about changes in the system. In between these events the system does not change radically. For a single-server queue, the events which change the system are the arrival of a new customer, or the completion of service of the customer being served. This latter event results in his departure. During the service of a customer we know what is going on and it is not necessary to record any further details. Only when the system changes must we update our records. We use a clock to record time and advance this clock to the time of the next event and record the changes that occur. Thus our clock does not advance by constant units, but by the steps which take us to the next event. The procedure can be illustrated schematically in the flow diagram which follows.

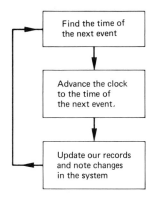

For a single-server queue the next event time (NET) will either be the next arrival time (NAT) or the next service completion time (NSCT). When we have had an arrival we make NET = NAT and find the time of the *next* arrival time as NAT + IAT, where IAT is a value from the distribution of inter-arrival times. When we have had a service completion we make NET = NSCT. If there are customers in the system we can then find NSCT as NET + DS where DS is a value from the distribution of service times. If however the system is left empty we have to wait until the next arrival before we can find his or her service completion time.

A flow chart with key to indicate the variables, and a program listing follow. The logic of the behaviour of the system is appropriate for the G/G/1 system. The inter-arrival times are obtained at subroutine 2000, the service times are obtained at subroutine 3000. With the subroutines in the listing it is the M/M/1 queue that is being considered, but these subroutines could be changed to deal with other cases. In updating the records, a count of arrivals and service completions is kept, along with the number in the system, the accumulated waiting time, queueing time, and the time the server is busy. These are then used to compute quantities such as the mean number in the system, the proportion of time the server is idle, etc. The output in the example given can be compared with the theoretical results from the tabulated values in Chapter 2.

The results are printed every 200 service completions so that the variation and *convergence* to the steady state can be observed. The target value for MNIS$\left(\dfrac{\rho}{1-\rho}\right)$ is 4; for PTSI it is $(1 - \rho)$, i.e. 0.2.

```
LIST
    20 SIMS=0
    40 PRINT"ENTER NOSMS":INPUT NOSMS
    80 PRINT"ENTER COUNT CONTROL":INPUT CO
   100 CN=CO:S=0:W=0:WQ=0:NAT=0:NET=0:TLE=0
   120 NSCT=0:CA=0:CS=0
   140 PRINT"ENTER NO. OF SERVICES":INPUT N
   160 PRINT"ENTER LAM":INPUT LAM
   180 PRINT"ENTER MU":INPUT MU:RHO=LAM/MU
   200 PRINT"ENTER INITIAL NIS":INPUT NIS
   240 PRINT"SINGLE SERVER QUEUE SIMULATION"
   260 PRINT"LAMBDA=";LAM:PRINT"MU=";MU
   280 PRINT"RHO=";RHO
   300 PRINT"       NSVS        MNIS     MNIQ     MTIS     MTIQ      PTSI"
   340 MAL=-1/LAM:UM=-1/MU
   400 GOSUB 2000
   420 NAT=NAT+IAT
   450 IF NIS>0 THEN GOTO 480
   460 NET=NAT
   480 GOSUB 3000:NSCT=DS+NET
   500 IF NAT>NSCT THEN GOTO 660
   520 NET=NAT:CA=CA+1
   540 W=W+NIS*(NET-TLE)
   560 IF NIS=0 THEN GOTO 620
   580 S=S+NET-TLE
   600 WQ=WQ+(NIS-1)*(NET-TLE)
   620 NIS=NIS+1:TLE=NET
   640 GOSUB 2000:NAT=NAT+IAT
   650 GOTO 500
   660 NET=NSCT:CS=CS+1
   680 W=W+NIS*(NET-TLE):S=S+NET-TLE
   700 IF NIS>0 THEN WQ=WQ+(NIS-1)*(NET-TLE)
   720 NIS=NIS-1:TLE=NET
   740 IF CS<CN THEN GOTO 900
   760 MW=W/CA:MQW=WQ/CA:MNIS=W/NET
```

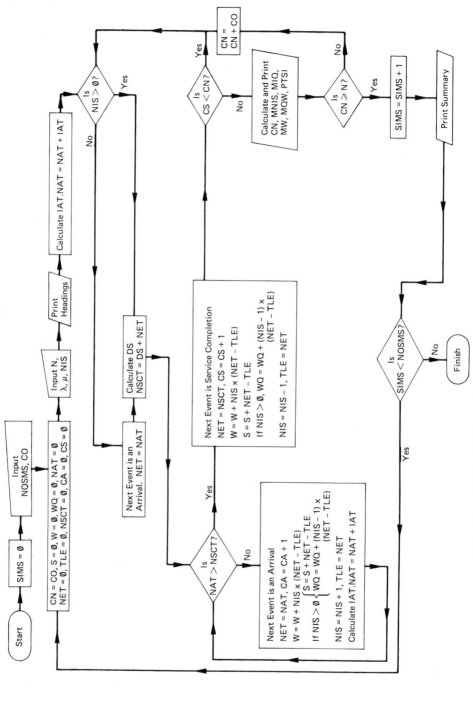

Flow Chart for Single-Server Queue Simulation – first come first served discipline

```
780 MIQ=WQ/NET:PTSI=(NET-S)/NET
800 @%=10:PRINT CN;"      ";:@%=&20308
820 PRINT MNIS,MIQ,MW,MQW,PTSI
840 PRINT""
860 IF CN>=N THEN GOTO 980
880 CN=CN+CO
900 GOTO 450
980 SIMS=SIMS+1
1000 PRINT"NO. OF ARRIVALS=";CA
1020 PRINT"DURATION OF SIMULATION=";TLE
1040 PRINT"SERVING TIME=";S
1080 IF SIMS<NOSMS THEN GOTO 100
1100 END
2000 IAT=MAL*LN(RND(1))
2100 RETURN
3000 DS=UM*LN(RND(1))
3100 RETURN


>RUN
ENTER NOSMS
?1
ENTER COUNT CONTROL
?200
ENTER NO. OF SERVICES
?2000
ENTER LAM
?0.8
ENTER MU
?1
ENTER INITIAL NIS
?4
SINGLE SERVER QUEUE SIMULATION
LAMBDA=0.8
MU=1
RHO=0.8
      NSVS    MNIS    MNIQ    MTIS    MTIQ    PTSI
       200   4.216   3.357   5.143   4.095   0.142
       400   3.471   2.649   4.419   3.374   0.179
       600   2.830   2.052   3.642   2.641   0.222
       800   2.995   2.212   3.861   2.851   0.217
      1000   3.060   2.274   3.958   2.941   0.214
      1200   3.251   2.464   4.247   3.219   0.213
      1400   4.049   3.249   5.243   4.206   0.199
      1600   3.975   3.178   5.141   4.110   0.203
      1800   3.834   3.038   4.941   3.916   0.204
      2000   3.819   3.024   4.922   3.898   0.205

NO. OF ARRIVALS=1999.000
DURATION OF SIMULATION=2576.658
SERVING TIME=2047.205
```

KEY

CA ≡ Counts arrivals
CN ≡ A counter to control output
CO ≡ Output is performed every CO services
CS ≡ Counts services
DS ≡ Duration of service (Service time)
IAT ≡ Inter-arrival time
LAM (BDA) ≡ Arrival rate (λ)
MAL ≡ $-1/\lambda$
MNIQ ≡ Mean number in queue (≡ MIQ)
MNIS ≡ Mean number in system
MTIQ ≡ Mean time in queue (≡ MQW)
MTIS ≡ Mean time in system (≡ MW)
MU ≡ Service rate (μ)
N ≡ Number of services per simulation
NAT ≡ Next arrival time
NET ≡ Next event time
NIS ≡ Number in the system
NOSMS ≡ Number of simulations to be done
NSCT ≡ Next service completion time
NSVS ≡ Number of services
PTSI ≡ Proportion of time server idle
RHO ≡ Traffic intensity (= λ/μ)
S ≡ Serving time
SIMS ≡ A counter for number of simulations
TLE ≡ Time of last event
UM ≡ $-1/\mu$
W ≡ Waiting time in system
WQ ≡ Waiting time in queue

It is possible to modify the program so that it gives a more physical representation of the system, and shows the changes in the system at the moments when these changes occur. The reader is urged to try this. Use will need to be made of the computer's timing device (most have one) and its graphics facilities. Coding is not given since this is not universal. The output shown illustrates results obtained from a PET.

The state of the system in terms of the customers in the system (the one being served being in reverse field) is shown. The computer will know the time and type (arrival or departure) of the next event, and waits the appropriate number of time units before displaying the new state.

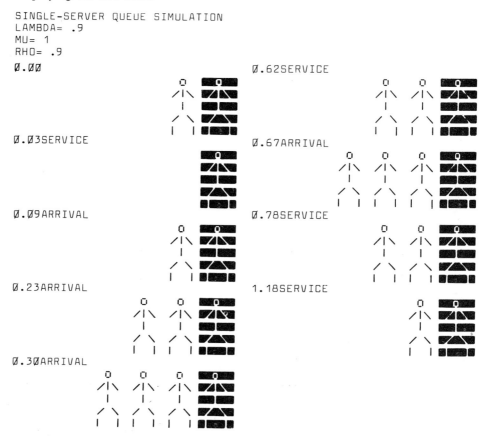

6.4 The G/G/*m* Queue

Most of the logic of the G/G/1 program can be incorporated into a program to simulate a queue with *m* (M) servers. Our record keeping needs to be more elaborate. We need an indicator BS(J) to indicate whether or not server J is busy; BS(J) = 1 indicates that he is busy, BS(J) = $\emptyset$ indicates that he is free. NSCT(J) will denote the next service completion time of server J when he is busy. The earliest (smallest) of these values will be the next service completion time NSCT. The label of the server who first completes service is L. NBS is used to denote the number of busy servers. The subroutines to generate inter-arrival and service times are at 4000 and 5000 respectively. In the listing they are appropriate to the M/M/m queue, so that the results can be checked against the theoretical values given at the end of Chapter 3.

The program given contains several REM statements to enable readers to follow the logic. It merits some study but could no doubt be modified and improved and readers are encouraged to try this. A specimen of the output is given and can be checked against the tabulated values in Chapter 3. The theoretical value in the last column, the proportion of time that a server is busy, is ρ/M [see Exercises 3, Question 18].

```
LIST
  20 PRINT"ENTER NO. OF SERVERS":INPUT R
  40 DIM NSCT(R), BS(R)
  60 SIMS=0:PRINT"ENTER NOSMS":INPUT NOSMS
 100 PRINT"ENTER COUNT CONTROL":INPUT CO
 120 CN=CO:S=0:W=0:WQ=0:NAT=0:NET=0:TLE=0:NSCT=0
 140 CA=0:CS=0:NQ=0:NBS=0:K=0
 160 FOR J=1 TO R:NSCT(J)=0:BS(J)=0:NEXT J
 180 PRINT"ENTER NO. OF SERVICES":INPUT N
 200 PRINT"ENTER LAM":INPUT LAM
 220 PRINT"ENTER MU":INPUT MU:RHO=LAM/MU
 240 PRINT"ENTER INITIAL NIS":INPUT NIS
 280 PRINT"MULTI-SERVER QUEUE SIMULATION"
 300 PRINT"LAMBDA=";LAM:PRINT"MU=";MU:PRINT"RHO=";RHO
 320 @%=&80002;PRINT"NUMBER OF SERVERS = ";R
 340 PRINT"     NSVS         MNIS     MNIQ     MTIS     MTIQ      PTSB"
 380 MAL=-1/LAM:UM=-1/MU
 390 REM ALLOCATE INITIAL CUSTOMERS TO SERVERS;
 391 REM FIND SERVICE COMPLETION TIMES.
 395 REM RECORD BUSY SERVERS AND NUMBER IN QUEUE.
 400 IF NIS>0 THEN K=NIS:NQ=0
 420 IF NIS>R THEN K=R:NQ=NIS-R
 440 NBS=K:IF K=0 THEN GOTO 600
 460 FOR J=1 TO K:GOSUB 5000:NSCT(J)=DS:BS(J)=1:NEXT J
 470 REM FIND NSCT AS EARLIEST SERVICE COMPLETION
 475 REM TIME & FIRST SERVER FREE(L)
 480 MI=1E30:L=0
 500 FOR J=1 TO K
 520 IF NSCT(J)>MI THEN GOTO 560
 540 MI=NSCT(J):L=J
 560 NEXT J
 580 NSCT=MI
 590 REM FIND TIME OF FIRST ARRIVAL.
 600 GOSUB 4000
 620 NAT=NAT+IAT
 630 REM & HIS SERVICE COMPLETION TIME IF SYSTEM IS EMPTY.
 635 REM SEND HIM TO SERVER 1
 640 IF NIS>0 THEN GOTO 800
 660 NET=NAT
 680 GOSUB 5000:NSCT(1)=NET+DS:BS(1)=1:NSCT=NSCT(1):L=1
 800 IF NAT>NSCT THEN GOTO 1200
 810 REM WE HAVE AN ARRIVAL.
 820 NET=NAT:CA=CA+1
 840 W=W+NIS*(NET-TLE)
 860 IF NIS=0 THEN GOTO 920
 880 IF NBS>0 THEN S=S+NBS*(NET-TLE)
 900 IF NBS=R AND NIS>R THEN WQ=WQ+(NIS-R)*(NET-TLE)
 920 NIS=NIS+1:TLE=NET
 940 IF NIS>R OR NIS=1 THEN GOTO 1060
 950 REM SEND ARRIVAL TO FIRST FREE SERVER;
 955 REM UPDATE RECORD ON SERVERS.
 960 FOR J=1 TO R
 980 IF BS(J)=1 THEN GOTO 1020
1000 GOSUB 5000:NSCT(J)=NET+DS:G=J:J=R:BS(G)=1:NBS=NBS+1
1020 NEXT J
```

```
1030 REM CHECK IS LAST ARRIVAL IS FIRST TO GO.
1040 IF NSCT>NSCT(G) THEN NSCT=NSCT(G):L=G
1050 REM UPDATE QUEUE SIZE IF NECESSARY.
1060 IF NIS>R THEN NQ=NIS-R
1080 IF NIS=1 THEN NBS=1
1100 GOSUB 4000:NAT=NAT+IAT
1120 GOTO 800
1190 REM WE HAVE SERVICE COMPLETION BY SERVER L.
1200 NET=NSCT:CS=CS+1
1220 W=W+NIS*(NET-TLE):S=S+NBS*(NET-TLE)
1240 IF NBS=R AND NIS>R THEN WQ=WQ+(NIS-R)*(NET-TLE):NQ=NQ-1
1260 NIS=NIS-1:TLE=NET:BS(L)=0:IF NBS>0 THEN NBS=NBS-1
1280 IF NIS<R THEN GOTO 1380
1290 IF NIS<R THERE IS NO QUEUE;OTHERWISE SEND NEXT CUSTOMER
TO FIRST FREE SERVER
1300 FOR J=1 TO R
1320 IF BS(J)=1 THEN GOTO 1360
1340 GOSUB 5000:NSCT(J)=NET+DS:G=J:J=R:BS(G)=1:NBS=NBS+1
1360 NEXT J
1380 IF CS<CN THEN GOTO 1600
1400 MW=W/CA:MQW=WQ/CA:MNIS=W/NET
1420 QM=WQ/NET:PTSB=S/(NET*R)
1440 @%=10:PRINT CN;"      ";:@%=&20308
1460 PRINT MNIS,QM,MW,MQW,PTSB
1480 PRINT""
1500 IF CN>=N THEN GOTO 2000
1520 CN=CN+CO
1600 IF NIS>0 THEN GOTO 1700:REM FIND FIRST FREE SERVER
1605 REM AND NSCT=MIN. OF NSCT(J).  OTHERWISE,
1610 REM SYSTEM IS EMPTY.  NEXT EVENT IS AN ARRIVAL,
1615 REM SEND HIM TO SERVER 1 AT 680
1620 GOTO 660
1690 REM FIND FIRST FREE SERVER(L), AND NSCT=MIN. OF NSCT(J).
1700 MI=1E30:L=0
1720 FOR J=1 TO R
1740 IF BS(J)=0 THEN GOTO 1800
1760 IF NSCT(J)>MI THEN GOTO 1800
1780 MI=NSCT(J):L=J
1800 NEXT J
1820 NSCT=MI
1840 GOTO 800
2000 SIMS=SIMS+1
2020 PRINT"NO. OF ARRIVALS=";CA
2040 PRINT"DURATION OF SIMULATION=";TLE
2060 IF SIMS<NOSMS THEN GOTO 100
2100 END
4000 IAT=MAL*LN(RND(1))
4020 RETURN
5000 DS=UM*LN(RND(1))
5020 RETURN


>RUN
ENTER NO. OF SERVERS
?3
ENTER NOSMS
?1
ENTER COUNT CONTROL
?200
ENTER NO. OF SERVICES
?3000
ENTER LAM
?2
ENTER MU
?1
ENTER INITIAL NIS
?3
MULTI-SERVER QUEUE SIMULATION
LAMBDA=2.000
MU=1.000
RHO=2.000
```

```
NUMBER OF SERVERS = 3
     NSVS        MNIS     MNIQ     MTIS     MTIQ     PTSB
      200        2.595    0.618    1.233    0.294    0.659
      400        2.702    0.711    1.317    0.347    0.663
      600        2.564    0.627    1.253    0.306    0.646
      800        2.749    0.765    1.364    0.379    0.661
     1000        2.978    0.934    1.460    0.458    0.682
     1200        2.877    0.848    1.406    0.414    0.676
     1400        2.905    0.870    1.426    0.427    0.678
     1600        2.935    0.891    1.438    0.437    0.681
     1800        2.865    .0.837   1.409    0.412    0.676
     2000        2.844    0.832    1.402    0.410    0.671
     2200        2.749    0.774    1.364    0.384    0.658
     2400        2.711    0.747    1.361    0.375    0.655
     2600        2.721    0.746    1.358    0.373    0.658
     2800        2.654    0.705    1.330    0.353    0.650
     3000        2.823    0.860    1.411    0.430    0.654

NO. OF ARRIVALS=3000.000
DURATION OF SIMULATION=1500.129
```

6.5   A Machine-Minding Problem

The machine interference problems discussed in Chapter 5 did not take into account the time taken by the operative in walking to stopped machines. In the problem considered now this time is included.

Suppose that the operative has charge of N identical machines which break down at random at rate B in running time. Suppose the machines are equally spaced round a circle and it takes time W for the operative to walk from one machine to the next and inspect the next machine. If this machine is found stopped the operative spends a constant time R in repairing this machine. The operative's mode of working is to patrol the machines uni-directionally and repair stopped machines. This is therefore an elaboration on the machine interference problem of Sections 5.1 and 5.2. A machine may have to wait for attention not simply because the operative is repairing another machine when it breaks down, but also because the operative is at a different location on his patrol when it breaks down.

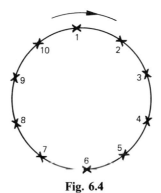

Fig. 6.4

We shall study the problem by simulation. In fact a theoretical solution was given by Mack, Murphy and Webb (1957), and a closely related problem, which arises in the textile industry, has been solved by Bunday and El-Badri (1984). The theory shows that the machine efficiency as defined in Chapter 5, the ratio of the actual total running time to that which would have been obtained had there been no stops, depends on the parameters N, B, W, R, not separately, but through the products BR and NBW. This might help the reader to understand why at lines 7∅ and 8∅ of the program which follows input of BR and NBW is requested with B and W being calculated at line 9∅. An equally valid alternative is to input B and W at lines 7∅ and 8∅ and compute BR and NBW at line 9∅. Indeed this may appear more natural.

A flow chart for the simulation, a key defining the variables, a listing of the program, and a specimen simulation follow. Run-times will be values from a negative exponential distribution with mean 1/B. Output is given every 200 time units (this could clearly be modified) and the *convergence* of the efficiency to its steady-state value can be observed. The theoretical value obtained by Bunday and El-Badri is 88.1. The first round is special. The operative goes round the machines and restarts them and the idle time (IDT) is considered to be zero at the end of this round. An alternative is to consider that the idle time should be given as

$$IDT = W + 2W + 3W + \cdots + (N - 1) \, W$$

at the end of the first round, these being the times for which the second, third, ..., Nth machines have to wait until they are started. Yet another idea to get round this 'end effect' is to do one simulation for a shift time and ignore it, but use the state in which the machines are left (hopefully something like the steady state) as the starting situation for the next simulation. The reader might consider the necessary modifications that should be made. At lines 33∅–36∅, (intermediate output), and 539–56∅, (final output), we update the total idle time by adding on the stopped time of all the machines which have not yet been inspected on the normal patrol.

In the example given the unit of time has been taken as the repair time. In typical applications in the textile industry, N could be anything from 2 to 30, R about 10 seconds, W up to about 5 seconds and B about 1 stop every 2 minutes (about 0.01 stops per second). Values for the products BR and NBW would be unlikely to exceed 0.25 in practice. It would be fairly unusual for a system with an efficiency of less than 60% to be run in a practical situation. These remarks might guide readers who wish to try the program.

KEY

$B \equiv$ Breakdown rate in running time per machine
$BR \equiv$ Product of breakdown rate and repair time
$BT(I) \equiv$ Breakdown time for machine I, (next time it stops)
$CT \equiv$ Intermediate output is printed every CT time units (approx.)
$EFF \equiv$ Machine efficiency as a percentage
$IDT \equiv$ Idle time of all the machines
$N \equiv$ Number of machines
$NBW \equiv$ Product of number of machines, breakdown rate and walking time
$NINS \equiv$ Number of inspections of machines
$NRP \equiv$ Number of repairs done
$OPT \equiv$ Operator's time (actual time)
$R \equiv$ Repair time
Run-time $\equiv$ The time for a machine to run from a repair to next breakdown
$SH \equiv$ Shift time (duration of simulation)
$T \equiv$ Total idle time including the waiting time of those machines which have not yet been repaired
$W \equiv$ Walking time from machine I to machine I + 1

Flow Chart for Simulation of N machines Uni-directionally patrolled by one operator when walking time and repair times are constant. Breakdowns occur at random so that Run-time has a negative exponential distribution

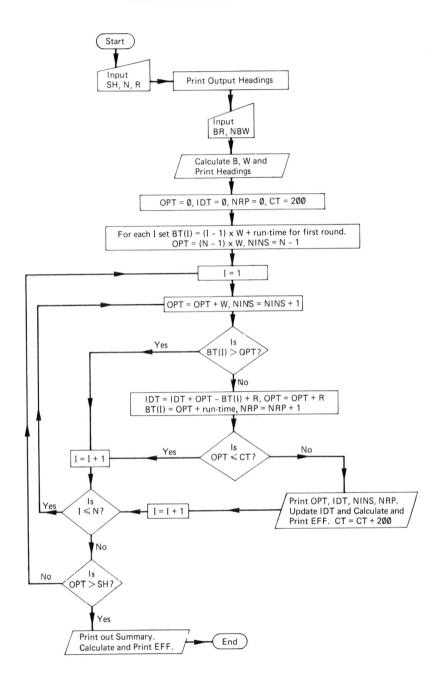

```
>LIST
   10 INPUT"SHIFT-TIME";SH
   20 INPUT"NO. OF MACHINES";N
   30 INPUT"REPAIR TIME";R
   50 PRINT"MACHINE EFFICIENCY,UNI-DIRECTIONAL PATROLLING"
   60 PRINT"CONSTANT WALKING TIME(W),CONSTANT REPAIR TIME(R)"
   70 PRINT"ENTER BR":INPUT BR
   80 PRINT"ENTER NBW":INPUT NBW
   90 B=BR/R:W=NBW/(N*B)
  100 PRINT"N= ";N;:PRINT"  BR= ";BR;::PRINT"  NBW= ";NBW
  110 PRINT"  OPTIME   IDTIME            NINS        NRP    EFF%"
  120 DIM BT(N)
  130 OPT=0:IDT=0:NRP=0:CT=200
  150 FOR I=1 TO N
  160 BT(I)=-(1/B)*LN(RND(1))+(I-1)*W
  170 NEXT I
  190 OPT=(N-1)*W:NINS=N-1
  200 FOR I=1 TO N
  210 OPT=OPT+W:NINS=NINS+1
  220 IF BT(I)>OPT THEN GOTO 420
  230 IDT=IDT+OPT+R-BT(I)
  240 OPT=OPT+R
  250 BT(I)=OPT-(1/B)*LN(RND(1))
  260 NRP=NRP+1
  270 IF OPT<=CT THEN GOTO 420
  290 @%=&20208:PRINT OPT,IDT;"   ";
  310 @%=10:PRINT NINS,NRP;
  330 T=IDT
  340 FOR J=1 TO N
  350 IF OPT>=BT(J) THEN T=T+OPT-BT(J)
  360 NEXT J
  370 EFF=100*(1-T/(N*OPT))
  390 @%=&20308:PRINT EFF
  400 CT=CT+200
  420 NEXT I
  430 IF OPT>=SH THEN GOTO 500
  450 IF OPT<SH THEN GOTO 200
  500 PRINT"SUMMARY"
  510 PRINT"SH= ";SH;::PRINT"  N= ";N
  520 PRINT"B= ";B;::PRINT"  R= ";R;::PRINT"   W= ";W
  525 PRINT"  BR= ";BR;::PRINT"  NBW= ";NBW
  530 T=IDT
  540 FOR J=1 TO N
  550 IF OPT>=BT(J) THEN T=T+OPT-BT(J)
  560 NEXT J
  570 EFF=100*(1-T/(N*OPT))
  580 PRINT"EFFICIENCY=";EFF;"%"
  600 END

>RUN
SHIFT-TIME?3600
NO. OF MACHINES?8
REPAIR TIME?1
MACHINE EFFICIENCY,UNI-DIRECTIONAL PATROLLING
CONSTANT WALKING TIME(W),CONSTANT REPAIR TIME(R)
ENTER BR
?0.05
ENTER NBW
?0.1
N= 8  BR= 5E-2  NBW= 0.1
  OPTIME   IDTIME          NINS        NRP     EFF%
  201.25  159.09          557          62     90.004
  400.50  355.42         1074         132     88.907
  607.00  560.24         1600         207     88.463
  802.00  759.25         2104         276     88.166
 1002.75  938.37         2635         344     88.303
 1201.00 1130.42         3136         417     88.235
 1400.50 1312.58         3662         485     88.285
 1602.50 1500.31         4182         557     88.297
 1800.50 1683.42         4702         625     88.309
 2005.50 1852.94         5246         694     88.446
 2203.75 2030.12         5771         761     88.485
 2400.25 2183.61         6309         823     88.628
```

```
2600.25 2382.64        6809       898   88.546
2800.50 2579.91        7326       969   88.475
3005.50 2763.33        7874      1037   88.506
3202.00 2956.78        8388      1105   88.455
3402.00 3175.82        8868      1185   88.331
3602.00 3363.72        9388      1255   88.327
SUMMARY
SH= 3600.000    N= 8.000
B= 0.050    R= 1.000    W= 0.250
  BR= 0.050    NBW= 0.100
EFFICIENCY=88.320%
```

6.6 Some General Remarks

The simulation which has been carried out for the systems of the previous three sections has produced results which can be compared with theoretical models. They are not spectacularly accurate and yet they represent a lot of work (by the computer). The exercise by which the behaviour of a physical system is transformed into a simulation program is a most important aspect of simulation modelling. The results which have been obtained suggest that further refinement would bring considerable benefit. The simple simulation models could well be improved by the introduction of some of the variance-reduction techniques, discussed for example, in Chapter 7 of the fine book by B. J. T. Morgan. For more complicated systems, it is desirable if not essential, to adopt a more structured approach, which involves such ideas as *activity cycle diagrams* and the *three phase method* as described in Chapters 3, 4 and 5 of the book, *Computer Simulation in Management Science*, by M. Pidd. Readers who wish to take their study of simulation further are recommended to try to incorporate some of these concepts into the programs of the text and in their solutions to the exercises.

However, it is still the case that a theoretical model is likely to give better results more easily than simulation. In the recently published work *Queueing Tables and Graphs* by Hillier and Yu it is stated 'Using Queueing Tables and Graphs, any practitioner can now model systems relevant to his needs without having to resort to *expensive* and *time consuming* simulation' (my italics). The search for good models for complicated systems must go on. Simulation is unlikely to be a panacea for all problems.

Exercises 6

1 Modify the program to simulate the single-server queue as indicated.

   (a) Use constant service with mean $1/\mu$ instead of exponential service with mean $1/\mu$.
   (b) Use the kth Erlang distribution with mean $1/\mu$ and variance $1/k\mu^2$ for service times. This can be generated as the sum of k independent exponential variables each with mean $1/k\mu$. [Exercises 1, Questions 3 and 4.]

In general the congestion will be least for constant service time ($k \to \infty$) and should decrease from its value for exponential service ($k = 1$) as k increases.

2 Modify the single-server queue simulation program so that instead of random arrivals at rate λ we have regular arrivals at rate λ so that the inter-arrival time is a constant $1/\lambda$. This again should reduce congestion.

3 Experiment with the programs for the single-server and many-server queues to simulate a variety of arrival and service patterns.

4 An operative looks after N identical machines which each fail at random in running time at average rate λ. Repair times are variable but have mean c. When a machine stops the operative repairs it if he is free. Otherwise he works on the machines in order of breakdown. Write a program to simulate this system. Choose the repair time distribution to be (a) exponential, (b) constant, (c) uniform in the range $\left(\dfrac{c}{2}, \dfrac{3c}{2}\right)$. In each case estimate the machine efficiency and comment on the results.

This of course is the classic machine interference problem as discussed in Chapter 5.

5 Repeat Question 4 in the case where a team of m operatives $(m \leqslant N)$ looks after the machines.

In particular try a variety of run-time distributions with exponential repair times. [N.B. Bunday and Scraton have shown that the efficiency for the G/M/r machine interference model is the same as that for the M/M/r machine interference model provided the average breakdown rate is the same in both cases.]

6 Customers to a single-server queue arrive at random at an average rate λ. Service has an exponential distribution with mean $1/\mu_1$. On being served the customers enter a second queue where service has an exponential distribution with mean $1/\mu_2$. This is an example of two queues in series.

$$\text{X} \quad \text{X} \quad \text{X} \quad \boxed{\text{X}} \quad \rightarrow \qquad \text{X} \quad \text{X} \quad \boxed{\text{X}}$$

1st Service	2nd Service
System 1	System 2

Simulate this system. Do you find that there are any conditions on λ, μ_1, μ_2 in order to get a steady-state solution? In the schematic representation estimate the mean number of customers in system 1 and in system 2. Estimate the mean time taken by a customer to pass through both systems. [See Saaty, Section 12.3.]

7 Customers to a queue arrive at random at average rate λ. There are two servers each giving exponential service at rate μ. If the system is empty an arriving customer chooses one of the servers at random. Otherwise he joins the shorter queue. If both queues are of equal length he chooses one of the servers at random. Write a program to simulate this system. Find the average time spent in the system by an arriving customer. [For a theoretical treatment see for example Haight or Kingman.]

8 A medical consultant spends on average 20 minutes with each patient, these times having a negative exponential distribution. Patients are scheduled to arrive at 14.00, 14.15, 14.30, 14.45, 15.00, 15.15 and 15.30. In fact they arrive at a time that is uniformly distributed throughout the 10 minute period before their scheduled appointment time. If the patient due to be seen has arrived and the consultant is free the consultant will see the patient even though this is before the scheduled time. Simulate the system and estimate the mean waiting time for patients. The first consultation starts promptly at 14.00. What is the probability that the consultant is still working at 16.30?

9 Consider the uni-directional patrolling problem discussed in Section 6.5. The complication considered by Bunday and El-Badri arises from the automatic nature of the repair involved. It is assumed that each attempt to repair a stopped machine has a probability Q of being successful. The time involved in the attempt is R whether or not the attempt is successful. If a machine is not repaired it has to remain stopped until next visited by the operative. For N in the range (2, 30), BR about 0.1, NBW about 0.1 and Q in the range (0.85, 0.95) simulate the system and estimate the efficiency. Target values may be found in the reference cited.

10 Bunday and El-Badri also considered the case where the operative repeatedly attempts to repair a stopped machine until successful. See the previous Question. They call this the 'repair until success' strategy. Simulate this system. For the same parameter values it should give a higher efficiency than that obtained in Question 9. Does your simulation confirm this?

11 A problem similar to that considered in Section 6.5 and with the complication of unsuccessful repairs as considered in Questions 9 and 10 arises in the case of an operative who cares for N identical machines which breakdown at random at rate B, when the machines are arranged in a line. The time to walk from one machine to the next is a constant W. The time to repair a stopped machine is a constant R. The operative walks from one end of the line of machines to the other and back again and so on. He repairs all stopped machines he finds.

Simulate this system with completely successful repairs (Q = 1) and with unsuccessful repairs (Q < 1). Estimate the efficiency. [Target values and the theoretical solution are to be found in the papers by Bunday and Mack, Bunday and Lee, and Bunday, El-Badri and Supanekar.]

12 For the single-server queue with random arrivals at average rate λ and exponential service at rate μ let $\rho = \lambda/\mu(< 1)$. A busy period for the server commences when he starts serving a customer following a period when the system was empty. The busy period ends when the server next becomes free for the first time. Simulate the system and estimate the mean length of a busy period. The theoretical value is $\frac{\rho}{\lambda(1-\rho)}$. [See also equation (7.15).] Estimate the mean number of customers who get served during a busy period. The theoretical value is $\frac{1}{(1-\rho)}$.

13 For the M/M/1 machine interference model use simulation to estimate the mean duration of the operative's busy period. Estimate the mean number of repairs completed during a busy period.

14   Question 1 of Exercises 4 [see also equations (4.14) and (4.15)] compares the M/M/1 system and the M/D/1 system. The arrival pattern is random at average rate λ in both cases. For negative exponential service the mean service time is $1/\mu$; for constant service time the service time is taken to be $1/\mu$ for the purposes of the comparison.

The theoretical models show that when ρ is near to 1, the average number in the M/D/1 system is about half that in the M/M/1 system. Does your simulation of the two systems confirm this result?

7
Transient Solutions and the Busy Period

7.1 A Theoretical Method

Most of the methods discussed in this book have concentrated on the calculation of the steady-state solution of a queueing system. In Section 2.1 we were able to obtain the time-dependent (transient) solution of the differential equations concerned, and from this it was possible to derive the steady-state probabilities. The problems are more of a technical nature than of a formulation or model building type. For the single-server queue with random arrivals and negative exponential service, we have, with the notation of Section 2.2, to solve the differential equations (2.19)

$$\left.\begin{aligned}
\frac{dp_0(t)}{dt} &= -\lambda p_0(t) + \mu p_1(t) \\
\frac{dp_1(t)}{dt} &= \lambda p_0(t) - (\lambda + \mu)\, p_1(t) + \mu p_2(t) \\
\frac{dp_2(t)}{dt} &= \lambda p_1(t) - (\lambda + \mu)\, p_2(t) + \mu p_3(t)
\end{aligned}\right\} \tag{7.1}$$

$$\text{etc.}$$

We have to find a solution to equations (7.1) for $p_0(t)$, $p_1(t)$, $p_2(t)$ etc., which satisfies some initial condition. For example if the system is empty at time zero, this initial condition would be $p_0(0) = 1$, $p_n(0) = 0$ for $n \neq 0$. The simple truth is that the task is not easy. It is possible to solve (7.1), (see the references for Chapter 2), but the methods are far from elementary.

We can adopt a similar approach in our consideration of the server's busy period. The busy period begins when the first customer enters the system and ends on the first occasion that the system is next empty. Thus we can regard the state with zero customers as an absorbing state (in the jargon of Markov Chains) so that as soon as the system enters this state no further transitions are possible from it and the busy period ends.

This means that we have to modify the first two equations in (7.1) and consider instead the system of differential equations:

$$\frac{dp_0(t)}{dt} = \mu p_1(t)$$

$$\frac{dp_1(t)}{dt} = -(\lambda + \mu)\, p_1(t) + \mu p_2(t) \tag{7.2}$$

- - - - - - - - - - - - - - - - - - -

$$\frac{dp_n(t)}{dt} = \lambda p_{n-1}(t) - (\lambda + \mu)\, p_n(t) + \mu p_{n+1}(t); \quad n \geqslant 2.$$

Once again the task of actually finding a solution, is far from trivial. The initial conditions will be $p_1(0) = 1$, $p_n(0) = 0$; $n \neq 1$ since the busy period starts with 1 in the system.

On the assumption that we have functions for $p_0(t)$, $p_1(t)$ etc. which satisfy equations (7.2) we see that if we consider the duration of the busy period to be a random variable T, with probability density function $h(t)$ and distribution function $H(t)$, then $p_0(t) = \Pr(T \leq t)$ (the probability that the system has reached state 0 by time t).

$$\therefore \quad H(t) = p_0(t). \tag{7.3}$$

Also

$$h(t) = \frac{dH(t)}{dt} = \mu p_1(t) \tag{7.4}$$

from the first of equations (7.2). Thus our solution describes the distribution of the busy period.

The cases where a time-dependent solution can be found are the exception rather than the rule. We show by means of an example a general approach which can often be successful. It follows the method developed in Section 1.5.

Example 1

Consider the birth–death equations with $\lambda_n = \lambda$ and $\mu_n = n\mu$, i.e. the self-service system of Section 3.2C. Let $p_n(t)$ be the probability that there are n customers in the system at time t and suppose there are i customers in the system initially; i.e. $p_n(0) = \delta_{in}$.

We have to solve the differential equations (a particular case of equations (3.3))

$$\left.\begin{aligned}
\frac{dp_0(t)}{dt} &= \qquad - \lambda p_0(t) \qquad + \qquad \mu p_1(t) \\
\frac{dp_n(t)}{dt} &= \lambda p_{n-1}(t) - (\lambda + n\mu) p_n(t) + (n+1)\mu p_{n+1}(t); \quad n \geq 1.
\end{aligned}\right\} \tag{7.5}$$

It is convenient to define the generating function

$$\pi(z, t) = \sum_{n=0}^{\infty} p_n(t) z^n. \tag{7.6}$$

If we multiply the equations of (7.5) by z^0, z, z^2 etc. and add we obtain

$$\sum_{n=0}^{\infty} z^n \frac{dp_n(t)}{dt} = \lambda \sum_{n=1}^{\infty} z^n p_{n-1}(t) - \lambda \sum_{n=0}^{\infty} z^n p_n(t)$$

$$- \mu \sum_{n=0}^{\infty} n z^n p_n(t) + \mu \sum_{n=0}^{\infty} (n+1) z^n p_{n+1}(t)$$

i.e.

$$\frac{\partial \pi(z, t)}{\partial t} = - \lambda(1 - z) \pi(z, t) + \mu(1 - z) \frac{\partial \pi(z, t)}{\partial z}$$

as careful consideration of the sums soon shows.

Thus $\pi(z, t)$ satisfies the partial differential equation

$$\frac{\partial \pi(z, t)}{\partial t} - \mu(1 - z) \frac{\partial \pi(z, t)}{\partial z} = - \lambda(1 - z) \pi(z, t). \tag{7.7}$$

Our problem is to solve equation (7.7) for $\pi(z, t)$ subject to the condition that $\pi(z, 0) = z^i$ where i is the initial number in the system. This follows since $\pi(z, 0) = \sum_{n=0}^{\infty} p_n(0) z^n$.

We do not have the space to embark on a detailed discussion of the methods available for the solution of partial differential equations. Suffice it to say that equation (7.7) is a particular case of what is known as Lagrange's Equation.

For the equation

$$P \frac{\partial \pi(z, t)}{\partial t} + Q \frac{\partial \pi(z, t)}{\partial z} = R$$

where P, Q, R are functions of π, z, t, we form the related equations

$$\frac{dt}{P} = \frac{dz}{Q} = \frac{d\pi}{R}.$$

If $u = u(t, z, \pi) = $ a constant and $v = v(t, z, \pi) = $ a constant are two particular integrals of these equations, then $u = f(v)$ where $f(\cdot)$ is an arbitrary function will give a solution of the partial differential equation. [See for example *Elements of Partial Differential Equations* by I. N. Sneddon, Chapter 2.] Thus for the equation

$$\frac{\partial \pi}{\partial t} - \mu(1 - z) \frac{\partial \pi}{\partial z} = - \lambda(1 - z) \pi$$

the related equations are

$$\frac{dt}{1} = \frac{dz}{-\mu(1 - z)} = \frac{d\pi}{-\lambda(1 - z)\pi}.$$

$$\frac{dt}{1} = \frac{dz}{-\mu(1 - z)} \quad \text{gives} \quad \frac{dz}{dt} = -\mu(1 - z)$$

which yields $u(z, t, \pi) = (1 - z)e^{-\mu t} = c_1$ (a constant).

$$\frac{dz}{\mu(1 - z)} = \frac{d\pi}{\lambda(1 - z)\pi} \quad \text{gives} \quad \frac{d\pi}{dz} = \frac{\lambda}{\mu} \pi$$

which yields $v(z, t, \pi) = \pi e^{-\frac{\lambda}{\mu} z} = c_2$ (a constant).

Thus the general solution of equation (7.7) is given by

$$v = g(u)$$

i.e. $\pi(z, t) = e^{\frac{\lambda}{\mu} z} g[(1 - z)e^{-\mu t}]$ where $g(\cdot)$ is an arbitrary function.

Now from the initial conditions, when $t = 0$,

$$\pi(z, 0) = z^i = e^{\frac{\lambda}{\mu} z} g(1 - z).$$

Then with $(1 - z) = y$, i.e. $z = 1 - y$

$$g(y) = e^{-\frac{\lambda}{\mu}(1 - y)}(1 - y)^i$$

and this gives the particular form that $g(\cdot)$ must have to satisfy the initial condition. We need $g[(1 - z)e^{-\mu t}]$.

Hence

$$\pi(z, t) = e^{\frac{\lambda}{\mu}z}\, e^{-\frac{\lambda}{\mu}[1 - (1 - z)e^{-\mu t}]}[1 - (1 - z)e^{-\mu t}]^i$$

$$\therefore \quad \pi(z, t) = \exp\left[-\frac{\lambda}{\mu}(1 - z)(1 - e^{-\mu t})\right]\{1 - (1 - z)e^{-\mu t}\}^i. \tag{7.8}$$

$$p_n(t) = \frac{1}{n!}\frac{\partial^n \pi}{\partial z^n}\bigg|_{z = 0}$$

$$= \frac{1}{n!}\sum_{k=0}^{n}\binom{n}{k}\left[\frac{\lambda}{\mu}(1 - e^{-\mu t})\right]^{n-k}\exp\left\{-\frac{\lambda}{\mu}(1 - e^{-\mu t})\right\}$$

$$\times \binom{i}{k}k!\,e^{-k\mu t}(1 - e^{-\mu t})^{i-k}$$

using Leibniz's result for the nth derivative of a product.

$$\therefore \quad p_n(t) = \frac{1}{n!}\exp\left\{-\frac{\lambda}{\mu}(1 - e^{-\mu t})\right\}\sum_{k=0}^{n}\binom{n}{k}\left(\frac{\lambda}{\mu}\right)^{n-k}(1 - e^{-\mu t})^{n - 2k + i}e^{-k\mu t}\binom{i}{k}k! \tag{7.9}$$

This is a somewhat intimidating expression. As $t \to \infty$, $e^{-\mu t} \to 0$ and the only term in the sum to survive is the one with $k = 0$.

Then for the steady-state solution

$$p_n = \operatorname*{Limit}_{t \to \infty} p_n(t) = \frac{1}{n!}\,e^{-\frac{\lambda}{\mu}}\left(\frac{\lambda}{\mu}\right)^n$$

which shows that after a long time the number in the system has a Poisson distribution with mean λ/μ. This is in agreement with the result of Section 3.2C. This is indeed the hard way to obtain the steady-state solution!

7.2   A Numerical Method

If we take the average service time $1/\mu$ as the unit of time, $\Big($equivalent to transforming to $\tau = \mu t$ so that $\dfrac{dp}{dt} = \dfrac{dp}{d\tau}\dfrac{d\tau}{dt} = \mu\dfrac{dp}{d\tau}$ and then writing t for $\tau\Big)$, equations (7.1) can be written in matrix form as

$$\frac{d\mathbf{P}(t)}{dt} = \mathbf{A}\mathbf{P}(t) \tag{7.10}$$

where

$$
P(t) = \begin{bmatrix} p_0(t) \\ p_1(t) \\ \vdots \\ p_n(t) \\ \vdots \end{bmatrix} \quad \text{and } A = \begin{bmatrix} -\rho & 1 & & & & 0 \\ \rho & -(1+\rho) & 1 & & & \\ & \rho & -(1+\rho) & 1 & & \\ & & \rho & -(1+\rho) & 1 & \\ 0 & & & \rho & -(1+\rho) & 1 \\ & & & & & \vdots \end{bmatrix} \quad (7.11)
$$

$P(t)$ is the vector of time-dependent probabilities; A is the *constant* matrix of transition probabilities ($\rho = \lambda/\mu$).

If the initial state probabilities are given as $P(0)$ then the solution of (7.10) can be written formally as

$$
P(t) = e^{At} P(0). \quad (7.12)
$$

$\left[\text{Compare this with the solution of the simple equation } \dfrac{dy}{dt} = ay; \text{ viz.} \right.$

$\left. y = y(0) e^{at}. \right]$

This result is to be found in many books on applications of the calculus, e.g. B. Porter, *Synthesis of Dynamical Systems*. Alternatively it can be thought of as the result of applying Picard's method. This takes the recurrence form

$$
P_{k+1}(t) = P(0) + \int_0^t AP_k(t)\, dt; \quad k = 0, 1, 2, \ldots \quad (7.13)
$$

$$
P_0(t) = P(0).
$$

Thus

$$
P_1(t) = P(0) + \int_0^t AP_0(t)\, dt
$$

$$
= (I + At)\, P(0)
$$

$$
P_2(t) = P(0) + \int_0^t AP_1(t)\, dt
$$

$$
= P(0) + \int_0^t A(I + At)\, P(0)\, dt
$$

$$
= \left(I + \frac{At}{1!} + A^2 \frac{t^2}{2!} \right) P(0) \text{ etc.}
$$

$$
P(t) = \underset{k \to \infty}{\text{Limit}} \left(I + A\frac{t}{1!} + A^2 \frac{t^2}{2!} + \cdots + A^k \frac{t^k}{k!} \right) P(0) \quad (7.14)
$$

Of course for our problem the dimensions of A are infinite. In order to obtain numerical values from equation (7.14) we must truncate A. We must also terminate the series (7.14) at a suitable value of k. Then we can obtain in a simple way a numerical solution which gives the values of $p_n(t)$ for various values of t and n. Readers familiar with numerical methods will point out that there are far better methods than Picard's for the numerical solution of differential equations. Your author agrees but, lacking space to embark on a discussion of the merits and details of such methods, is content to choose one that suffices to illustrate the (fairly rapid) convergence of the transient solution to the steady state.

A BASIC program to implement Picard's method for the solution of equation (7.10) in the form (7.14) is given along with the output from a particular run. The size of A is determined by N at line 2∅. As given, and with C = 0.000001 at line 8∅, the program calculates the probabilities to this accuracy. It prints out the values of $p_0(t)$, $p_1(t)$, $p_2(t)$ for $t = 0, 1, \ldots, 9$ (average service times). For the example given the convergence of the probabilities to their steady-state values, viz. $0.9, 0.09, 0.009, \ldots$, is apparent even with this rather crude approach. For values of $\rho \geqslant 1$ no steady state exists.

The reader is warned that Picard's method and its present implementation is not good enough computationally to deal with all cases, particularly for ρ much greater than about 0.8. However, it does enable us in the simpler situations to see the convergence to the steady state. Better numerical methods are needed for a more robust program. Readers expert in numerical analysis will be in a position to substitute such methods. Others may be consoled that it is not a vital issue at this juncture.

```
>LIST
  1∅ PRINT"TRANSIENT SOLUTION FOR A SIMPLE QUEUE"
  15 REM INPUT N,THE SIZE OF THE MATRIX A
  2∅ INPUT"N=    ";N
  3∅ DIM P∅(N),P(N),Q(N),R(N)
  4∅ DIM A(N,N)
  5∅ INPUT "RO=    ";RO
  6∅ PRINT"RO=    ";RO
  7∅ PRINT"     T          P∅(T)       P1(T)       P2(T)"
  75 @%=82∅6∅7
  8∅ C=∅.∅∅∅∅∅1
  9∅ REM SET UP P∅ &A
 1∅∅ FOR I=∅ TO N:P∅(I)=∅
 11∅ FOR J=∅ TO N:A(I,J)=∅
 12∅ NEXT J:NEXT I
 13∅ P∅(∅)=1
 15∅ A(∅,∅)=-RO:A(∅,1)=1
 16∅ FOR I=1 TO N-1
 17∅ A(I,I-1)=RO:A(I,I)=-(1+RO):A(I,I+1)=1
 28∅ NEXT I
 19∅ A(N,N-1)=RO:A(N,N)=-(1+RO)
 2∅∅ FOR T=∅ TO 9
 22∅ K=∅:REM K COUNTS THE NUMBER OF TERMS
 24∅ FOR I=∅ TO N:P(I)=P∅(I):Q(I)=P∅(I):NEXT I
 26∅ K=K+1:S=∅:SK=T/K
 28∅ FOR I=∅ TO N:R(I)=∅
 3∅∅ FOR J=∅ TO N:R(I)=R(I)+A(I,J)*Q(J):NEXT J:NEXT I
 32∅ FOR I=∅ TO N:Q(I)=R(I)*SK:P(I)=P(I)+Q(I):IF ABS(Q(I))>C THEN S=S+1
 33∅ REM THE NEXT TERM IS IN Q(I);
 335 REM IF EACH COMPONENT IS >C FIND THE NEXT TERM.
 34∅ NEXT I
 35∅ REM IF S>∅ THEN NOT ALL COMPONENTS ARE SMALL ENOUGH.
 36∅ IF S>∅ THEN GOTO 26∅
 4∅∅ PRINT T,P(∅),P(1),P(2)
 42∅ NEXT T
 45∅ END
```

```
>RUN
TRANSIENT SOLUTION FOR A SIMPLE QUEUE
N= ?10
RO= ?0.1
RO= 0.100000
     T          P0(T)          P1(T)          P2(T)
0.000000     1.000000       0.000000       0.000000
1.000000     0.938597       0.058880       0.002447
2.000000     0.916237       0.078175       0.005291
3.000000     0.907323       0.085116       0.007033
4.000000     0.903485       0.087839       0.007973
5.000000     0.901728       0.088990       0.008461
6.000000     0.900884       0.089508       0.008715
7.000000     0.900464       0.089752       0.008847
8.000000     0.900248       0.089871       0.008917
9.000000     0.900136       0.089933       0.008955
```

The same ideas can be used to obtain a numerical solution of equations (7.2) having first transformed them so that they contain the parameter ρ only. Then using equations (7.3) and (7.4) we can derive the distribution of the duration of the busy period in numerical form. This is left as an exercise for the reader. The analytic form of the solution is indeed complicated and involves Bessel functions. Of course some might argue that if numerical values are required, a direct numerical solution is more suitable than a very complicated formula [(7.9) for example], which poses very considerable problems when we try to evaluate it.

We can however, and by an elementary argument, obtain a simple formula for the mean length of a busy period for the single-server queue. Over a long period of time T there will be say N free periods and an equal number N of busy periods. The N free periods will last for a total time N/λ (asymptotically) if the arrivals occur at random at average rate λ. But since the probability that the server is free is $(1 - \rho)$ this will be $(1 - \rho)\,T$.

$$\therefore \quad (1 - \rho)\,T = \frac{N}{\lambda}$$

whence $N = \lambda(1 - \rho)\,T$.

The N busy periods must therefore last for a time ρT so that the mean duration of a busy period is

$$\frac{\rho T}{\lambda(1 - \rho)\,T} = \frac{1}{\mu(1 - \rho)}. \tag{7.15}$$

For the machine interference problem of Chapter 5, with one operative in charge of N machines where each machine breaks down at random at average rate λ and repair times have a negative exponential distribution with mean $1/\mu$, the birth–death equations with $\lambda_n = \lambda(N - n)$ and $\mu_n = \mu$ model the transient solution. If the mean repair time is taken to be the unit of time we can write these differential equations as [$\rho = \lambda/\mu$ as usual]:

$$\frac{d\boldsymbol{P}(t)}{dt} = \boldsymbol{B}\boldsymbol{P}(t) \tag{7.16}$$

where

$$\boldsymbol{P}^T(t) = (p_0(t), p_1(t), \dots, p_N(t)) \tag{7.17}$$

$$B = \begin{pmatrix} -N\rho & 1 & & & & & \\ N\rho & -[(N-1)\rho+1] & 1 & & & \mathbf{0} & \\ & (N-1)\rho & -[(N-2)\rho+1] & 1 & & & \\ \hline & & & & 3\rho & -(2\rho+1) & 1 \\ & \mathbf{0} & & & & 2\rho & -(\rho+1) & 1 \\ & & & & & & \rho & -1 \end{pmatrix}. \quad (7.18)$$

For the busy period we have to solve the equations

$$\frac{\mathrm{d}\boldsymbol{P}(t)}{\mathrm{d}t} = \boldsymbol{C}\boldsymbol{P}(t) \qquad (7.19)$$

with initial conditions $p_1(0) = 1$, $p_j(0) = 0$ for $j \neq 1$ where

$$C = \begin{pmatrix} 0 & 1 & & & & & \\ 0 & -[(N-1)\rho+1] & 1 & & & \mathbf{0} & \\ & (N-1)\rho & -[(N-2)\rho+1] & 1 & & & \\ \hline & & & & 3\rho & -(2\rho+1) & 1 \\ & \mathbf{0} & & & & 2\rho & -(\rho+1) & 1 \\ & & & & & & \rho & -1 \end{pmatrix}. \quad (7.20)$$

Readers are invited to write BASIC programs to solve these *finite* sets of equations. An analytic solution in a neat closed form has not yet been found. Programs to solve

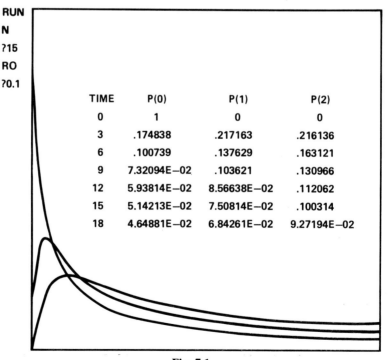

TIME	P(0)	P(1)	P(2)
0	1	0	0
3	.174838	.217163	.216136
6	.100739	.137629	.163121
9	7.32094E−02	.103621	.130966
12	5.93814E−02	8.56638E−02	.112062
15	5.14213E−02	7.50814E−02	.100314
18	4.64881E−02	6.84261E−02	9.27194E−02

RUN
N
?15
RO
?0.1

Fig. 7.1

equation (7.16), when initially all machines are running, and using a Runge–Kutta method and a Runge–Kutta–Merson method have been written. They also use the computer's graphic facilities. The output, the graphs of $p_0(t)$, $p_1(t)$, and $p_2(t)$, along with their tabulated values are shown in Fig. 7.1, for the case $N = 15$ and $\rho(\equiv RO) = 0.1$. The convergence to the steady-state solution as given in Chapter 5 is apparent.

For equations (7.19) with $N = 6$ and $\rho = 0.2$, the numerical and graphical solution is shown in Fig. 7.2. $p_0(t)$ represents the distribution function and $p_1(t)$ the density function for the duration of a busy period.

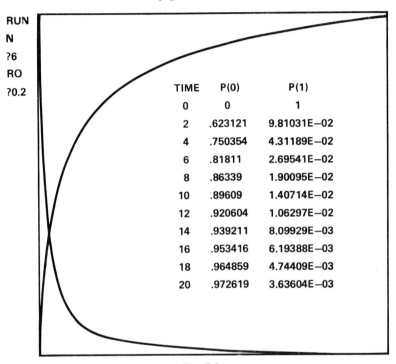

RUN			
N			
?6			
RO			
?0.2	TIME	P(0)	P(1)
	0	0	1
	2	.623121	9.81031E−02
	4	.750354	4.31189E−02
	6	.81811	2.69541E−02
	8	.86339	1.90095E−02
	10	.89609	1.40714E−02
	12	.920604	1.06297E−02
	14	.939211	8.09929E−03
	16	.953416	6.19388E−03
	18	.964859	4.74409E−03
	20	.972619	3.63604E−03

Fig. 7.2

7.3 The Number Served in a Busy Period

We consider once again the M/M/1 queue and consider a busy period during which time service is always going on.

We confine our attention to those epochs at which either a new customer arrives or a service is completed. The probability of an arrival in $(t, t + \delta t)$ is $\lambda \delta t + \circ(\delta t)$; the probability of a service completion in $(t, t + \delta t)$ is $\mu \delta t + \circ(\delta t)$. Thus given that one of these two events has occurred at a particular epoch, the probability that it is an arrival is $\lambda/(\lambda + \mu)$, and the probability that it is a service completion is $\mu(\lambda + \mu)$. Thus if we let x denote the number of service completions and y the number of customers in the system, we can represent the behaviour of the system at a succession of such epochs by means of a random walk on a two-dimensional lattice (Fig. 7.3).

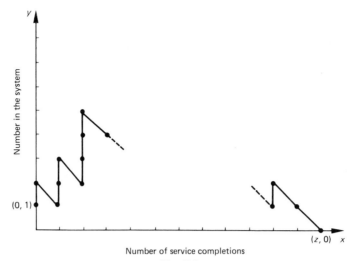

Fig. 7.3

$$\Pr\{(x, y) \rightarrow (x+1, y-1)\} = \frac{\mu}{\mu+\lambda} = \frac{1}{1+\rho}$$

$$\text{where } \rho = \frac{\lambda}{\mu}. \qquad (7.21)$$

$$\Pr\{(x, y) \rightarrow (x, y+1)\} \quad = \frac{\lambda}{\mu+\lambda} = \frac{\rho}{1+\rho}$$

If we restrict our attention to a busy period of the server, then the walk will begin at the point $(0, 1)$ when the first customer arrives, and will end at some point $(z, 0)$ where z represents the number of customers served during the busy period. Thus the x-axis will act as an absorbing barrier for the walk. Provided $\rho < 1$ the busy period will be sure to end after a finite number of services.

Let $P(z|x, y)$ denote the probability that starting from (x, y) the walk terminates at $(z, 0)$. Then since equations (7.21) describe the possible transitions

$$P(z|x, y) = \frac{1}{1+\rho} P(z|x+1; y-1) + \frac{\rho}{1+\rho} P(z|x, y+1). \qquad (7.22)$$

Further since

$$P(z+a|x+a, y) = P(z|x, y) \quad \text{for all } a \geqslant 0$$

we let $Q(z-x, y) = P(z|x, y)$.

$Q(\xi, \eta)$ is the probability that starting with η customers in the system, ξ more service completions occur before the busy period ends. Then from equation (7.22)

$$Q(x, y) = \frac{1}{1+\rho} Q(x-1, y-1) + \frac{\rho}{1+\rho} Q(x, y+1); \quad x, y \geqslant 1 \qquad (7.23)$$

with boundary conditions

$$Q(x, 0) = 0 \text{ for } x \neq 0, \quad Q(0, y) = 0 \text{ for } y \neq 0, \quad Q(0, 0) = 1$$

$$Q(x, y) = 0 \text{ for } x < y, \quad Q(x, x) = \left(\frac{1}{1+\rho}\right)^x.$$

We have to solve the partial difference equation (7.23) subject to these boundary conditions.

We define the generating function

$$\pi(s, t) = \sum_{x=1}^{\infty} \sum_{y=1}^{\infty} Q(x, y) s^x t^y \quad \text{for } 0 < \frac{s}{t} < 1. \tag{7.24}$$

Multiplication of equation (7.23) by $s^x t^y$ followed by summation over all values of $x, y \geqslant 1$ gives after a little algebra

$$(1 + \rho) \pi(s, t) = st + st\pi(s, t) + \frac{\rho}{t}\left[\pi(s, t) - \sum_{\xi=1}^{\infty} Q(\xi, 1) s^\xi t\right]$$

i.e. $\quad (1 + \rho) t\pi(s, t) = st^2[1 + \pi(s, t)] + \rho\pi(s, t) - \rho t G(s) \tag{7.25}$

where

$$G(s) = \sum_{\xi=1}^{\infty} Q(\xi, 1) s^\xi. \tag{7.26}$$

Now since the busy period commences with the arrival of the first customer, $Q(\xi, 1)$ is the probability that a busy period contains ξ service completions. Thus $G(s)$ is the probability generating function for the distribution of the number of service completions in a busy period for the M/M/1 queue.

From equation (7.25)

$$\pi(s, t) = \frac{t[st - \rho G(s)]}{-st^2 + (1 + \rho) t - \rho}. \tag{7.27}$$

However

$$\sum_{\xi=1}^{\infty} Q(\xi, 2) s^\xi = [G(s)]^2. \tag{7.28}$$

For the number served during a period which commences with 2 customers in the system we ignore one of them and consider the number served up to the moment when there are none in the system (except the one ignored). This constitutes the number served in a busy period, and then another busy period commences, the customer hitherto ignored initiating it.

A similar argument shows that

$$\sum_{\xi=1}^{\infty} Q(\xi, \eta) s^\xi = [G(s)]^\eta$$

Thus

$$\pi(s, t) = \sum_{\eta=1}^{\infty} [G(s) t]^\eta = \frac{tG(s)}{1 - tG(s)}. \tag{7.29}$$

From equations (7.27) and (7.29) we obtain

$$\rho[G(s)]^2 - (1+\rho)\, G(s) + s = 0$$

whence

$$G(s) = \frac{(1+\rho) - [(1+\rho)^2 - 4\rho s]^{\frac{1}{2}}}{2\rho} \tag{7.30}$$

and we have taken the root that is 1 when $s = 1$.

The power series expansion of (7.30) readily yields, after a little algebra

$$Q(\xi, 1) = \frac{1}{2}\binom{2\xi}{\xi} \frac{\rho^{\xi-1}}{(1+\rho)^{2\xi-1}} \cdot \frac{1}{2\xi-1} \quad \text{for } \xi \geqslant 1 \tag{7.31}$$

and so gives the distribution of the number of customers served during a busy period.

For the M/G/1 model the number of customers in the system at the termination of a service is a random variable Y. We consider the value of Y at successive completion-of-service times. If S is the number of customers who arrive during a service time and $\Pr(S = s) = p_s$, then we can represent the behaviour of the system at these completion-of-service times as a random walk on a two-dimensional lattice. X represents the number of service completions, Y the number in the system. As X changes from x to $x + 1$, Y changes from y to $y + s - 1$ with probability p_s (see Fig. 7.4).

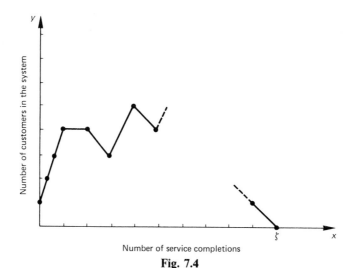

Fig. 7.4

The busy period will commence at a point $(0, 1)$ and terminate when first Y is 0 at some point $(\xi, 0)$. The value ξ will be the number of customers served in the busy period.

We let S have probability generating function

$$\Phi(z) = \sum_{s=0}^{\infty} p_s z^s. \tag{7.32}$$

[This is equivalent to equation (4.23).]

Rather than just concentrating on the busy period we generalise to the situation where we start with C customers in the system, i.e. the walk starts at the point $(0, C)$. The probability that starting from this situation it first reaches the axis after N service completions is denoted by $U(N, C)$.

Then

$$U(N+1, C+1) = \sum_{s=0}^{N-C} p_s U(N, C+s) \tag{7.33}$$

which follows from consideration of what happens during the first service time in which s customers arrive and 1 is served.

The $U(N, C)$ must satisfy the boundary conditions

$$U(N, 0) = 0 \text{ for } N \geqslant 1; \quad U(0, 0) = 1; \quad U(N, C) = 0 \text{ for } N < C \tag{7.34}$$

and

$$U(N, N) = p_0^N.$$

Now $U(1, 0)$ and $U(1, 1)$ are known. Then equations (7.33) and (7.34) either determine $U(2, 0)$, $U(2, 1)$ and $U(2, 2)$ directly or enable them to be found from the values p_0, p_1, p_2 etc. Then $U(3, 0)$, $U(3, 1)$, ..., $U(3, 3)$ can be found etc. Thus equations (7.33) and (7.34) define $U(N, C)$ uniquely.

It is convenient to write

$$U(N, C) = p_0^C V(N - C, C). \tag{7.35}$$

Thus we obtain from equation (7.33)

$$V(X, C+1) = \sum_{s=0}^{N-C} \lambda_s V(X-s, C+s) \tag{7.36}$$

where

$$\lambda_s = p_s p_0^{s-1}. \tag{7.37}$$

Here

$$V(X, 0) = 0 \text{ for } X \geqslant 1; \quad V(X, C) = 0 \text{ for } X < 0; \quad V(0, C) = 1 \tag{7.38}$$

which follows from equation (7.34).

Then we show that we can write $V(X, C)$ as

$$V(X, C) = C \sum^{\{x\}} \frac{\lambda_1^{\alpha_1} \lambda_2^{\alpha_2} \cdots}{\alpha_1! \alpha_2! \cdots} \cdot \frac{(C + X - 1)!}{(C + X - \Sigma \alpha_i)!} \tag{7.39}$$

where $\{1^{\alpha_1}, 2^{\alpha_2}, \ldots\}$ is a partition of X and $\sum^{\{x\}}$ means summation over all such partitions.

The solution (7.39) clearly satisfies the boundary conditions. It also satisfies the partial difference equation (7.36). We first note that every partition of $X - s$ where $s \geqslant 1$ can be obtained from those partitions of X in which $\alpha_s \geqslant 1$ by reducing α_s by 1. Thus, for $s \geqslant 1$ we obtain from equation (7.39)

$$V(X - s, C + s) = (C + s) \sum_{\alpha_s \geqslant 1}^{\{x\}} \frac{\alpha_s / \lambda_s}{\alpha_1! \, \alpha_2! \ldots} \lambda_1^{\alpha_1} \lambda_2^{\alpha_2}$$

$$\ldots \frac{(C + X - 1)!}{(C + X - \Sigma \alpha_i + 1)!}.$$

We note that the condition $\alpha_s \geqslant 1$ can be removed since any term in which $\alpha_s = 0$ becomes zero anyway. Thus the R.H.S. of the partial difference equation (7.36) becomes

$$\sum^{\{x\}} \frac{\lambda_1^{\alpha_1} \lambda_2^{\alpha_2} \ldots}{\alpha_1! \, \alpha_2! \ldots} \cdot \frac{(C + X - 1)!}{(C + X - \Sigma \alpha_i + 1)!} \cdot \left\{ \sum_{s=1}^{\infty} (C + s) \alpha_s + C(C + X - \Sigma \alpha_i + 1) \right\}$$

$$= \sum^{\{x\}} \frac{\lambda_1^{\alpha_1} \lambda_2^{\alpha_2} \ldots}{\alpha_1! \, \alpha_2! \ldots} \cdot \frac{(C + X - 1)!}{(C + X - \Sigma \alpha_i + 1)!} \cdot (C + X)(C + 1)$$

(since $\Sigma s \alpha_s = X$ for a partition of X),

$$= (C + 1) \sum^{\{x\}} \frac{\lambda_1^{\alpha_1} \lambda_2^{\alpha_2} \ldots}{\alpha_1! \, \alpha_2! \ldots} \cdot \frac{(C + X)!}{(C + 1 + X - \Sigma \alpha_i)!}$$

$$= V(X, C + 1) \text{ as required.}$$

Thus

$$V(X, C) = \frac{C}{C + X} \sum^{\{x\}} \frac{\lambda_1^{\alpha_1} \lambda_2^{\alpha_2} \ldots}{\alpha_1! \, \alpha_2! \ldots} \cdot \frac{(C + X)!}{(C + X - \Sigma \alpha_i)!} \tag{7.40}$$

$$= \text{Coefficient of } z^x \text{ in } \frac{C}{C + X} (1 + \lambda_1 z + \lambda_2 z^2 + \cdots)^{C + X}$$

$$= \text{Coefficient of } z^x \text{ in } \frac{C}{C + X} [(\Phi(p_0 z) / p_0]^{C + X}$$

$$= \text{Coefficient of } z^x \text{ in } \frac{C}{(C + X) \, p_0^C} [\Phi(z)]^{C + X}.$$

Hence

$$U(N, C) = \text{coefficient of } z^{N - C} \text{ in } \frac{C}{N} [\Phi(z)]^N. \tag{7.41}$$

This is a reasonable way in which to calculate $U(N, C)$, the probability that starting with C customers in the system the busy period lasts through N more service completions.

For the busy period $C = 1$ and so

$$U(N, 1) = \text{coefficient of } z^{N - 1} \text{ in } \frac{1}{N} [\Phi(z)]^N. \tag{7.42}$$

For the M/M/1 machine interference problem with N identical machines, if we confine our attention to those epochs at which either a machine stops or a repair is completed, then the behaviour of the system during a busy period can be represented by a random walk on a two-dimensional lattice. We let x denote the number of repairs completed and y the number of machines running. Then for two successive epochs

$$\Pr\{(x, y) \to (x+1, y+1)\} = \frac{\mu}{\mu + y\lambda} = \frac{\gamma}{\gamma + y}; \quad x \geqslant 0, 0 \leqslant y < N \qquad (7.43)$$

$$\Pr\{(x, y) \to (x, y-1)\} \quad = \frac{y\lambda}{\mu + y\lambda} = \frac{y}{\gamma + y}; \quad x \geqslant 0, 0 < y \leqslant N \qquad (7.44)$$

where

$$\gamma = \frac{\mu}{\lambda}.$$

All other transitions have zero probability. The walk is illustrated in Fig. 7.5. The busy period starts at the point $(0, N-1)$ and terminates at the point (z, N) where z is the value of x on the first occasion that y is N, and so represents the number of repairs completed in the busy period.

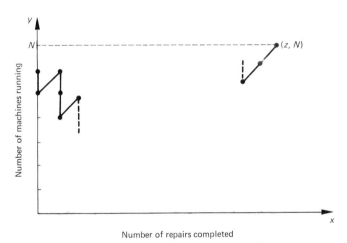

Fig. 7.5

If $r(z|x, y)$ denotes the probability that starting from (x, y) the walk finishes at (z, N) then we obtain

$$r(z|x, y) = \frac{\gamma}{\gamma + y} r(z|x+1, y+1) + \frac{y}{\gamma + y} r(z|x, y-1) \qquad (7.45)$$

for

$$x \geqslant 0, 0 \leqslant y \leqslant N-1$$

with boundary conditions

$$\left. \begin{array}{ll} r(z|x, N) = \delta_{x, z} & \\ r(z|x, y) = 0 & \text{for } z - x < N - y \\ r(z|x, y) = \dfrac{\gamma}{\gamma + y} \cdot \dfrac{\gamma}{\gamma + y + 1} \cdots \dfrac{\gamma}{\gamma + N - 1} & \text{for } z - x = N - y. \end{array} \right\} \qquad (7.46)$$

An analytical solution to the equation (7.45) satisfying the boundary conditions (7.46) is not easy to find. (See the exercises, Question 16 onwards.) However, for a given value of $z(=z_0$ say) and given values for γ and N it is easy to solve these equations numerically and from this to derive the distribution of the number of repairs completed in a busy period as far as the value z_0. The BASIC program shown will compute the values $r(z|x, y)$ for $0 \leqslant y \leqslant N$ and $0 \leqslant x \leqslant z_0$, for input values of γ (G) and z_0. The reader will need to format his own output.

```
>LIST
   20 PRINT"PROGRAM FOR R(Z/X,Y)"
   40 INPUT "G= ";G
   60 INPUT "Z= ";Z
   70 INPUT "N= ";N
   80 DIM R(Z,N)
  100 PRINT"                    R(Z/X,Y)"
  120 PRINT" Y                    X"
  130 @%=&20003
  140 FOR I=0 TO Z:PRINT"    ";I;:NEXT I
  160 PRINT""
  200 FOR X=0 TO Z:FOR Y=0 TO N:R(X,Y)=0:NEXT Y:NEXT X
  220 R(Z,N)=1
  240 FOR X=Z-1 TO 0 STEP -1
  260 M=Z-X:K=N-M
  280 IF K<0 THEN K=0
  300 FOR Y=K TO N-1
  320 IF Y=0 THEN R(X,Y)=G*R(X+1,Y+1)/(G+Y):GOTO 360
  340 R(X,Y)=(G*R(X+1,Y+1)+Y*R(X,Y-1))/(G+Y)
  360 NEXT Y
  380 NEXT X
  400 FOR Y=N TO 0 STEP -1
  420 @%=&20003:PRINT Y;:@%=&20305
  440 FOR X=0 TO Z
  460 PRINT R(X,Y);" ";
  480 NEXT X:PRINT""
  500 NEXT Y
  600 END
```

```
>RUN
PROGRAM FOR R(Z/X,Y)
G= ?5
Z= ?10
N= ?6
                    R(Z/X,Y)
 Y                    X
     0.    1.    2.    3.    4.    5.    6.    7.    8.    9.    10.
 6 0.000 0.000 0.000 0.000 0.000 0.000 0.000 0.000 0.000 0.000 1.000
 5 0.015 0.018 0.022 0.027 0.032 0.041 0.053 0.077 0.139 0.500 0.000
 4 0.030 0.036 0.044 0.053 0.065 0.081 0.106 0.154 0.278 0.000 0.000
 3 0.046 0.055 0.066 0.079 0.095 0.116 0.143 0.174 0.000 0.000 0.000
 2 0.061 0.073 0.087 0.102 0.119 0.132 0.124 0.000 0.000 0.000 0.000
 1 0.075 0.090 0.105 0.120 0.127 0.103 0.000 0.000 0.000 0.000 0.000
 0 0.090 0.105 0.120 0.127 0.103 0.000 0.000 0.000 0.000 0.000 0.000
```

```
>RUN
PROGRAM FOR R(Z/X,Y)
G= ?10
Z= ?10
N= ?4
                    R(Z/X,Y)
 Y                    X
     0.    1.    2.    3.    4.    5.    6.    7.    8.    9.    10.
 4 0.000 0.000 0.000 0.000 0.000 0.000 0.000 0.000 0.000 0.000 1.000
 3 0.000 0.000 0.000 0.001 0.003 0.008 0.020 0.051 0.148 0.769 0.000
 2 0.000 0.001 0.002 0.005 0.013 0.033 0.085 0.220 0.641 0.000 0.000
 1 0.001 0.002 0.006 0.015 0.039 0.100 0.253 0.583 0.000 0.000 0.000
 0 0.002 0.006 0.015 0.039 0.100 0.253 0.583 0.000 0.000 0.000 0.000
```

For the case $N = 6$, $\gamma = 5$ ($\rho = 0.2$ in our usual notation) Table 7.1 shows the values of $r(15|x, y)$. For the same values of N and γ Table 7.2 shows the values $r(z|0, 5)$ for values of $z = 1, 2, \ldots, 24$. These give the probabilities that the number of repairs completed in a busy period is z. It should be clear how these values are obtained from an extended Table 7.1.

Table 7.1 $r(15|x, y)$

y	0	1	2	3	4	5	6	7	8	9	10	11	12	13	14	15
5	.006	.007	.009	.011	.013	.015	.018	.022	.027	.032	.041	.053	.077	.139	.500	0
4	.012	.015	.018	.021	.025	.030	.036	.044	.053	.065	.081	.106	.154	.278	0	0
3	.018	.022	.026	.032	.038	.046	.055	.066	.079	.095	.116	.143	.174	0	0	0
2	.024	.029	.035	.042	.051	.061	.073	.087	.102	.119	.132	.124	0	0	0	0
1	.030	.037	.044	.053	.063	.075	.090	.105	.120	.127	.103	0	0	0	0	0
0	.037	.044	.053	.063	.075	.090	.105	.120	.127	.103	0	0	0	0	0	0

x

Table 7.2 $r(z|0, 5)$

$r(z|0, 5)$	.500	.139	.077	.053	.041	.032	.027	.022	.018	.015	.013	.011
z	1	2	3	4	5	6	7	8	9	10	11	12

$r(z|0, 5)$	.009	.007	.006	.005	.004	.004	.003	.002	.002	.002	.001	.001
z	13	14	15	16	17	18	19	20	21	22	23	24

Exercises 7

1   Consider the birth–death system with $\lambda_n = \lambda$, $\mu_n = n\mu$. [Example 1 of Section 2.1.] Use the result (7.8)

$$\pi(z, t) = \exp\left[-\frac{\lambda}{\mu}(1 - z)(1 - e^{-\mu t}) \right]\{1 - (1 - z)e^{-\mu t}\}^i$$

to show that if there are i customers in the system initially then the expected number in the system at time t is

$$L(t) = \frac{\partial \pi}{\partial z}\bigg|_{z=1} = \frac{\lambda}{\mu}(1 - e^{-\mu t}) + i e^{-\mu t}.$$

2   With reference to Question 1 above use the equations (7.5) to show that if

$$L(t) = \sum_0^\infty n p_n(t)$$

then

$$\frac{dL(t)}{dt} = \lambda - \mu L(t).$$

Deduce that if the system has i customers in it initially, then

$$L(t) = \frac{\lambda}{\mu} (1 - e^{-\mu t}) + i e^{-\mu t}.$$

3 Obtain $\underset{t \to \infty}{\text{Limit}} \, \pi(z, t)$ where $\pi(z, t)$ is given by equation (7.8). Deduce the steady-state probabilities p_n for the self-service system.

4 A telephone exchange has N lines. On each line the time intervals between calls is exponentially distributed with mean $1/\lambda$ and the length of calls is distributed exponentially with mean $1/\mu$. [Calls not connected immediately are lost to the system.]
If $p_n(t)$ denotes the probability that n lines are in use at time t show that

$$\frac{dp_n(t)}{dt} = (N - n + 1) \lambda p_{n-1}(t) - [(N - n) \lambda + n\mu] p_n(t) + (n + 1) \mu p_{n+1}(t)$$

for $1 \leqslant n \leqslant N - 1$

and obtain equations for $\dfrac{dp_0(t)}{dt}$ and $\dfrac{dp_N(t)}{dt}$.

If $\pi(z, t) = \sum\limits_{n=0}^{N} p_n(t) z^n$ show that

$$\frac{\partial \pi(z, t)}{\partial t} - (1 - z)(\mu + \lambda z) \frac{\partial \pi(z, t)}{\partial z} + N\lambda(1 - z) \pi(z, t) = 0.$$

Show that the solution corresponding to no lines being used initially is

$$\pi(z, t) = \left\{ \frac{(\mu + \lambda e^{-(\lambda + \mu) t}) + \lambda z(1 - e^{-(\lambda + \mu) t})}{\lambda + \mu} \right\}^N$$

and hence find an expression for the mean number of lines in use at time t.

5 For the birth–death process if $\lambda_n = n\mu$, $\mu_n = n\mu$ and i customers are in the system at time $t = 0$ show that

$$\pi(z, t) = \sum\limits_{n=0}^{\infty} p_n(t) z^n = \left\{ \frac{\mu[1 - e^{(\lambda - \mu) t}] - z[\lambda - \mu e^{(\lambda - \mu) t}]}{\mu - \lambda e^{(\lambda - \mu) t} - \lambda z[1 - e^{(\lambda - \mu) t}]} \right\}^i.$$

Show that when $i = 1$

$$p_n(t) = [1 - p_0(t)] \left[1 - \frac{\lambda - \lambda e^{(\lambda - \mu) t}}{\mu - \lambda e^{(\lambda - \mu) t}} \right] \left[\frac{\lambda - \lambda e^{(\lambda - \mu) t}}{\mu - \lambda e^{(\lambda - \mu) t}} \right]^{n-1}$$

$$p_0(t) = \frac{\mu e^{(\lambda - \mu) t} - \mu}{\lambda e^{(\lambda - \mu) t} - \mu}.$$

If $N (= N(t))$ is the number in the system at time t verify that

$$E(N) = e^{(\lambda - \mu) t}$$

$$\text{Var}(N) = \frac{\lambda + \mu}{\lambda - \mu} e^{(\lambda - \mu) t} [e^{(\lambda - \mu) t} - 1].$$

6 For the M/M/N machine interference problem with a team of N operatives looking after N machines, show that the equations for the time-dependent probabilities $p_n(t)$, that n machines are stopped at time t are identical to those obtained in Question 4. The $\pi(z, t)$ corresponds to the situation where all machines are running initially. Deduce that in this case

$$p_n(t) = \binom{N}{n} \left\{ \frac{\lambda}{\lambda + \mu} (1 - e^{-(\lambda + \mu)t}) \right\}^n \left\{ \frac{\mu + \lambda e^{-(\lambda + \mu)t}}{\lambda + \mu} \right\}^{N-n}.$$

Can you use equations (2.9) and (2.10) with $p_R(0) = 1$ and $p_S(0) = 0$ to obtain this result by an elementary argument?

Deduce the steady-state solution for p_n as given by equations (5.22) and (5.23) when $m = N$.

Deduce this last result also, by showing that

$$\operatorname*{Limit}_{t \to \infty} \pi(z, t) = \left(\frac{\mu + \lambda z}{\lambda + \mu} \right)^N.$$

7 A model suggested for the reproduction by binary fission of bacteria is as follows: growth of the cell involves replication of N genes within the cell. When all N genes have been replicated the cell divides and the process repeats itself.

Let $X(t)$ be the number of genes which have been replicated in a cell of age t. Let $\Pr[X(t) = n]$ be $p_n(t)$.

Then (under certain assumptions to be stated)

$$\frac{dp_n(t)}{dt} = -\lambda(N - n) p_n(t) + \lambda(N - n + 1) p_{n-1}(t).$$

If $p_n(0) = 1, \ n = 0$;
$\qquad \ \ = 0, \ n > 0$;

show that

$$p_n(t) = (-1)^n \binom{N}{n} e^{-N\lambda t}(1 - e^{\lambda t})^n.$$

Hence find the density function for the random variable τ, the age of a cell when it divides.

8 Write a program to find a numerical solution of equations (7.1), (7.2), (7.16) and (7.19). This will enable you to compute the transient solution and the distribution of the busy period duration for the M/M/1 system and the M/M/1 machine interference problem. You may use Picard's method which will suffice for a limited range of values. A superior numerical method would be a Runge–Kutta or a Runge–Kutta–Merson method. If in doubt don't be afraid to seek the help and advice of a numerical analyst. He might need some assistance with a queueing problem one day.

9 Incorporate the graphics facilities of your computer in your program from Question 8 and construct the graphs of the functions involved. (See Figs 7.1 and 7.2.)

10 Apply your program to the M/M/m machine interference problem with N machines to investigate the transient solution and the busy period duration. Are the steady-state probabilities becoming apparent?

11   Apply your program to the self-service system of Example 1, Section 7.1. Can you obtain the correct numerical values for the steady-state probabilities?

12   Use equation (7.30) to show that the mean number of customers served during a busy period is

$$G'(s)|_{s=1} = \frac{1}{1-\rho}.$$

13   Use equation (7.30) to verify equation (7.31). Use the result obtained in Question 12 to show that the variance of the number of customers served during a busy period for the M/M/1 queue is

$$\frac{\rho + \rho^2}{(1-\rho)^3}.$$

14   For the single-server queue with random arrivals at rate λ and exponential service at rate μ ($\rho = \lambda/\mu$) show that $\Phi(z)$ as given by equation (7.32) takes the form

$$\Phi(z) = \frac{1}{(1+\rho - \rho z)}.$$

Deduce that $u(\xi, 1)$ as given by equation (7.42) is

$$u(\xi, 1) = \frac{1}{\xi}\left(\frac{-\xi}{\xi - 1}\right)\left(\frac{1}{1+\rho}\right)^{\xi}\left(\frac{-\rho}{1+\rho}\right)^{\xi-1}$$

$$= \frac{1}{2}\left(\frac{2\xi}{\xi}\right)\frac{\rho^{\xi-1}}{(1+\rho)^{2\xi-1}} \cdot \frac{1}{2\xi - 1}$$

in accord with equation (7.31).

15   For the single-server queue with random arrivals at rate λ and constant service time b ($\rho = \lambda b < 1$) show that $\Phi(z)$ as given by equation (7.32) takes the form

$$\Phi(z) = e^{-\rho(1-z)}.$$

Deduce an expression for the probability that N customers are served in a busy period for the M/D/1 system.

16   Show that $r(z + a|x + a, y) = r(z|x, y)$ in the notation of equation (7.45). Deduce that if

$$Q(z - x, y) = r(z|x, y)$$

then $Q(m, n)$ denotes the probability that starting with n machines running, the busy period lasts through m more repairs.
    Show that

$$Q(m, N) = \delta_{m,0}; \quad Q(0, n) = \delta_{n, N}; \quad Q(m, N) = 0 \quad \text{if } m < N - n$$

$$Q(N - n, n) = \frac{\gamma}{\gamma + n} \cdot \frac{\gamma}{\gamma + n + 1} \cdots \frac{\gamma}{\gamma + N - 1}$$

and

$$(\gamma + n)\, Q(m, n) = \gamma Q(m - 1, n + 1) + nQ(m, n - 1); \quad 0 \leqslant n \leqslant N - 1.$$

Let

$$\sum_{m=0}^{\infty} Q(m, n) \, s^m \equiv s^{N-n} \, V_n(s) \quad \text{for } 0 \leqslant n \leqslant N - 1,$$

and $V_N(s) = 1$.

Show that

$$(\gamma + n) \, V_n(s) = \gamma V_{n+1}(s) + ns V_{n-1}(s); \quad 0 \leqslant n \leqslant N - 1$$

$$V_N(s) = 1.$$

Show that there is a solution of the form

$$V_n(s) = T_n(s) \, V_0(s)$$

so that

$$T_0(s) = 1, \quad T_1(s) = 1$$

and $\qquad T_{n+1}(s) = \dfrac{\gamma + n}{\gamma} T_n(s) - \dfrac{ns}{\gamma} T_{n-1}(s) \quad \text{for } n = 1, 2, 3, \ldots, N - 1.$

17 Use the results of Question 16 to show that

$T_n(s)$ is of degree $\left[\dfrac{n}{2}\right]$ in s, $T_n(1) = 1$ for all n, $T_n(s)$ is independent of N.

Deduce that $\qquad\qquad\qquad V_n(s) = \dfrac{T_n(s)}{T_N(s)}.$

Evaluate $T_2(s)$, $T_3(s)$, $T_4(s)$ etc.

18 For the busy period we are interested in the generating function

$$\sum_{m=0}^{\infty} Q(m, N-1) \, s^m = \dfrac{s T_{N-1}(s)}{T_N(s)}.$$

For the mean number of repairs completed in a busy period

$$E\{M\} = \dfrac{d}{ds} \left[\dfrac{s T_{N-1}(s)}{T_N(s)} \right]_{s=1}.$$

Show that $\qquad\qquad E(M) = 1 - \{T_N'(1) - T_{N-1}'(1)\}$

$$= 1 - M_N \text{ say.}$$

Deduce that $\qquad M_{n+1} = \dfrac{n}{\gamma} (M_n - 1) \quad \text{for } n = 1, 2, 3, \ldots.$

Hence find $E(M)$.

References

Chapter 1

1 E. Brockmeyer, H. L. Halstrom and A. Jensen, *The Life and Works of A. K. Erlang*, (all of Erlang's papers translated into English), Copenhagen Telephone Company, Copenhagen, 1948.

Chapter 2

2 A. B. Clarke, 'On the Solution of the "Telephone Problem"', *Univ. Michigan Eng. Res. Inst. Rept.*, R-32, March 1952.
3 A. B. Clarke, 'The Time Dependent Waiting Line Problem', Univ. Michigan Rept., M720-IR39, 1953.
4 S. Karlin and J. McGregor, 'The Classification of Birth and Death Processes', *Trans. Am. Math. Soc.*, **86**, 1957, pp. 366–400.
5 S. Karlin and J. McGregor, 'The Differential Equations of Birth and Death Processes and the Stieltjes Moment Problem', *Trans. Am. Math. Soc.*, **85**, 1957, pp. 489–546.
6 G. E. H. Reuter, 'Denumerable Markov Processes and the Associated Contraction Semigroups on 1', *Acta Math.*, **97**, 1957, pp. 1–46.
7 F. S. Hillier and O. S. Yu, *Queueing Tables and Graphs*, North Holland, 1984.

Chapter 4

8 D. G. Kendall, 'Some Problems in the Theory of Queues', *J. Roy. Stat. Soc. B*, **13**, 1951, pp. 151–5.
9 D. G. Kendall, 'Stochastic Processes Occurring in the Theory of Queues and their Analysis by Means of the Imbedded Markov Chain', *Ann. Math. Statist.*, **24**, 1953, pp. 338–54.

Chapter 5

10 H. Ashcroft, 'The Productivity of Several Machines Under the Care of One Operator', *J. Roy. Stat. Soc. B*, **12** (1), 1950, pp. 145–51.
11 F. Benson and D. R. Cox, 'The Productivity of Machines Requiring Attention at Random Intervals', *J. Roy. Stat. Soc. B*, **13**, 1951, pp. 65–82.
12 B. D. Bunday and R. E. Scraton, 'The $G/M/r$ Machine Interference Model', *Eur. J. Op. Res.*, **4**, 1980, pp. 399–402.
13 C. Mack and K. D. C. Stoodley, 'Machine Interference with Two Repairmen when Repair Time is Constant', *New J. Statist. and Op. Res.*, **4** (2), 1968, pp. 1–7.
14 D. G. Maritas and D. A. Xirokostas, 'The $M/E_k/r$ Machine Interference Model', *Eur. J. Op. Res.*, **1**, 1977, pp. 112–23.
15 L. G. Peck and R. N. Hazelwood, *Finite Queueing Tables*, ORSA Publications in Operations Research 2, Wiley, New York, 1958.

Chapter 6

16 G. E. P. Box and M. E. Müller, 'A Note on the Generation of Random Normal Deviates', *Ann. Math. Stat.*, **29**, 1958, pp. 610–11.

17 B. D. Bunday and W. K. El-Badri, 'A Model for a Textile Winding Process', *Eur. J. Op. Res.*, **15**, 1984, pp. 55–62.

18 B. D. Bunday, W. K. El-Badri and S. D. Supanekar, 'The Efficiency of Bi-directionally Patrolled Machines When Repairs Are Not Always Successful', *Eur. J. Op. Res.*, **19**, 1985, pp. 324–30.

19 B. D. Bunday and R. Lee, 'The Efficiency of a Textile Winding Process', *J. Roy. Stat. Soc. Ser. C*, **27**, 1978, pp. 305–09.

20 B. D. Bunday and C. Mack, 'Efficiency of Bi-directionally Traversed Machines', *J. Roy. Stat. Soc. Ser. C*, **22**, 1973, pp. 74–81.

21 F. A. Haight, 'Two Queues in Parallel', *Biometrika*, **45**, 1958, pp. 401–10.

22 J. M. Hammersley and D. C. Handscomb, *Monte Carlo Methods*, Methuen, London, 1964.

23 J. F. C. Kingman, 'Two Similar Queues in Parallel', *Ann. Math. Stat.*, **32**, 1961, pp. 1314–23.

24 B. J. T. Morgan, *Elements of Simulation*, Chapman and Hall, London, New York, 1984.

25 C. Mack, T. Murphy and N. L. Webb, 'The Efficiency of *N* Machines Uni-directionally Patrolled by One Operative when Walking Time and Repair Times are Constants', *J. Roy. Stat. Soc.*, **19**, 1957, pp. 166–72.

26 M. Pidd, *Computer Simulation in Management Science*, John Wiley, 1984.

27 T. Saaty, *Elements of Queueing Theory*, McGraw Hill, London, New York, Toronto, 1961.

28 K. D. Tocher, *The Art of Simulation*, EUP, 1969.

Chapter 7

29 S. Barnett and C. Storey, *Matrix Methods in Stability Theory*, Nelson, 1970.

30 B. D. Bunday and W. K. El-Badri, 'The Busy Period for the M/M/1 Machine Interference Model', *Stoch. An. and App.*, **3** (No. 1), 1985, pp. 1–13.

31 B. Porter, *Synthesis of Dynamical Systems*, Nelson, 1969.

32 M. G. Smith, *Introduction to the Theory of Partial Differential Equations*, Van Nostrand, 1967.

33 I. N. Sneddon, *Elements of Partial Differential Equations*, McGraw Hill, 1957.

Suggestions for Further Reading

The enormous bibliography of papers on queueing theory has already been mentioned. The references given should enable the student to trace the applications to their original source but they are a very restricted subset of possible references. Many books on the mathematical methods of Operational Research include chapters on queueing theory. They are unlikely to add much to the contents of this book except to show wider applications. The reader anxious to progress may find the following advanced texts a valuable source of theory, applications and bibliography.

J. W. Cohen, *The Single Server Queue*, North Holland, 1969.

B. Conolly, *Lecture Notes on Queueing Theory*, Ellis Horwood, 1975.

R. B. Cooper, *Introduction to Queueing Theory*, Edward Arnold, 1981.

D. R. Cox and W. L. Smith, *Queues*, Chapman and Hall, 1961.

A. Lee, *Applied Queueing Theory*, Macmillan, 1966.

G. F. Newell, *Applications to Queueing Theory*, Chapman and Hall, 1982 (Applications to Traffic).

N. U. Prabhu, *Queues and Inventories*, J. Wiley, 1965.

T. L. Saaty, *Elements of Queueing Theory*, McGraw Hill, 1961.

R. Syski, *Introduction to Congestion Theory in Telephone Systems*, Oliver and Boyd, 1960.

Answers to Exercises

Exercises 1

6 $\mu[t]$; $\sigma^2[t]^2$ where $[t] \equiv$ integer part of t.
Poisson, mean $\mu[t]$.

Exercises 2

2 $\lambda p_R T$; $\lambda c p_R T$. **4** Yes; No.

5 $\dfrac{\mathrm{d}p(t)}{\mathrm{d}t} = \lambda - (\lambda + \mu) p(t)$; $p(t) = \dfrac{\lambda}{\lambda + \mu} + \dfrac{\mu \, \mathrm{e}^{-(\lambda + \mu) t}}{\lambda + \mu}$.

7 $p_n = (1 - \rho) \rho^n$. **9** $\dfrac{1}{5}$; 4.

10 Yes, it saves £50 per week.

11 20 minutes; $\dfrac{32}{243}$. **12** $p_E(t) = \dfrac{\lambda}{\lambda + \mu} + \dfrac{\mu \, \mathrm{e}^{-(\lambda + \mu) t}}{\lambda + \mu}$.

13 $L_1 = 1$, $L_{q_1} = \frac{1}{2}$, $W_{q_1} = 5$ minutes; $L_2 = \frac{1}{2}$, $L_{q_2} = \frac{1}{6}$, $W_{q_2} = 2\frac{1}{2}$ minutes, $L = 5$,
$L_q = 4\frac{1}{6}$, $W_q = 25$ minutes.

15 (a) ρ (b) $\dfrac{1}{\mu - \lambda}$ (c) $\dfrac{\mu}{\mu - \lambda}$.

17 On assumption of random arrivals and exponential service $L_q = 8\frac{1}{9} (> 5)$ and the proportion of time the device will be in use is 75%. The assumption of exponential service is very dubious. Constant service time might be more likely.

18 $\mu = \lambda + \sqrt{\dfrac{C\lambda}{S}}$.

20 No. The average queueing time and time in the system would be doubled. The average queueing time and time in the system would be increased by a factor n.

Exercises 3

3 $p_0 = 1/(1 + 3\rho + 6\rho^2 + 6\rho^3)$
Average no. running $= 3(1 + 2\rho + 2\rho^2)/(1 + 3\rho + 6\rho^2 + 6\rho^3)$.

4 $p_0 = 1/(1 + N\rho + N(N-1)\rho^2 + N(N-1)(N-2)\rho^3 + \cdots + N!\,\rho^N)$

Average no. running

$$= \frac{N[1 + (N-1)\rho + (N-1)(N-2)\rho^2 + \cdots + (N-1)!\,\rho^{N-1}]}{1 + N\rho + N(N-1)\rho^2 + \cdots + N!\,\rho^N}$$

5 $p_n = (n+1)(1-\rho)^2\,\rho^n.$

6 $\frac{1}{5}$, 4. Probably. The savings amount to £300 per week.

7 $p_n = \dfrac{p_0(kC)^n}{\sqrt{n!}}$ where $p_0 =$ proportion of time server is free

$$= 1 \Big/ \left\{ 1 + kC + \frac{(kC)^2}{\sqrt{2!}} + \frac{(kC)^3}{\sqrt{3!}} + \cdots \right\}.$$

8 $p_n = \dfrac{e^{-\frac{\lambda}{\mu}}\left(\dfrac{\lambda}{\mu}\right)^n}{n!}.$

9 (i) $p_0 = 1 \Big/ \left\{ 1 + \rho + \dfrac{\rho^2}{2!} + \cdots + \dfrac{\rho^N}{N!} \right\}$ where $\rho = \dfrac{\lambda}{\mu}$

(ii) $p_{N-1} = \dfrac{p_0\,\rho^{N-1}}{(N-1)!}$ (iii) $p_N = \dfrac{p_0\,\rho^N}{N!}.$

10 $\frac{1}{15}$; weekly expected profit without land = £245; with land = £244.03; No.

11 Weekly expected profit is now £251.27; Yes.

12 (i) $\frac{4}{3}$ (ii) $\frac{1}{3}$ (iii) $\frac{1}{2}$.

13 Queueing times 3 mins, $\frac{4}{3}$ mins; $\frac{2}{3}$ mins for two-server queue.

14 $(0.8)^7 \simeq 0.21$; 0.952; 0.0146.

15 $\frac{1}{7}, \frac{1}{4}$, 0.77 minutes.

17 (i) $\frac{1}{11}$ (ii) $\frac{5}{33}$ (iii) $\frac{25}{33}\cdot\frac{5}{3}$; $\frac{5}{3}$.

Exercises 4

2 0.2, 1.805, 9.025 minutes.

4 The mean time in the queue is 14.5 minutes so it seems likely that a reasonable proportion will have to wait for 15 minutes or more. [It is being assumed that the doctor who carries out the first phase of service is also involved in the second.]

6 $L_q = \dfrac{\lambda^2}{2\mu(\mu - \lambda)}, \quad L = \dfrac{\lambda}{\mu} + \dfrac{\lambda^2}{2\mu(\mu - \lambda)}$

$\left.\vphantom{\begin{array}{c} \\ \\ \\ \\ \end{array}}\right\}$ where $\dfrac{1}{\mu}$ is the service time

$W_q = \dfrac{\lambda}{2\mu(\lambda - \lambda)}, \quad W = \dfrac{1}{\mu} + \dfrac{\lambda}{2\mu(\mu - \lambda)}$

or

$L_q = \dfrac{\lambda \rho b}{2(1 - \rho)}, \quad L = \rho + \dfrac{\lambda \rho b}{2(1 - \rho)}$

$\left.\vphantom{\begin{array}{c} \\ \\ \\ \\ \end{array}}\right\}$ where b is the service time and $\rho = \lambda b$.

$W_q = \dfrac{\rho b}{2(1 - \rho)}, \quad W = b + \dfrac{\rho b}{2(1 - \rho)}$

7 $\frac{16}{7}$ minutes.

8 Mean $= \dfrac{\rho b}{2(1 - \rho)}$, Variance $= \dfrac{b^2(4\rho - \rho^2)}{12(1 - \rho)^2}$ where $\rho = \lambda b$.

9 $\dfrac{2\rho - \rho^2}{2(1 - \rho)}$.

10 $\dfrac{2\lambda}{\mu} < 1, \ Q(z) = \dfrac{\mu^2\left(1 - \dfrac{2\lambda}{\mu}\right)}{\mu^2 - \lambda(\lambda + 2\mu)\,z + \lambda^2\,z^2}$; Mean $= \dfrac{\lambda(2\mu - \lambda)}{\mu(\mu - 2\lambda)}$.

16 0.8, 0.62863.

Exercises 5

4 (a) $\dfrac{N\rho + N(N - 1)\rho^2 + \cdots + N!\,\rho^N}{1 + N\rho + N(N - 1)\rho^2 + \cdots + N!\,\rho^N}$

(b) $\dfrac{1 + (N - 1)\rho + (N - 1)(N - 2)\rho^2 + \cdots + (N - 1)!\,\rho^{N-1}}{1 + N\rho + N(N - 1)\rho^2 + \cdots + N!\,\rho^N}$.

5 4 machines.

6 $\dfrac{3(a - a^2 + a^3)}{[1 + 3\lambda c(a - a^2 + a^3)]}$.

9 $p_0 = 1 \Big/ \left(\displaystyle\sum_{n=0}^{M} \binom{N}{n}\left(\dfrac{\lambda}{\mu}\right)^n + \sum_{n=M+1}^{N} \dfrac{N!}{(N-n)!\,M!} \cdot \dfrac{\left(\dfrac{\lambda}{\mu}\right)^n}{M^{n-M}} \right)$

$p_n = \binom{N}{n} \dfrac{\lambda^n \mu^{N-n}}{(\lambda + \mu)^N}$

Mean no. stopped $= \dfrac{N\lambda}{\lambda + \mu}$.

Exercises 7

3 $\pi(z) = \exp\left[-\dfrac{\lambda}{\mu}(1 - z)\right]$ for any value of i, $p_n = \dfrac{e^{-\frac{\lambda}{\mu}}\left(\dfrac{\lambda}{\mu}\right)^n}{n!}$.

4 $\dfrac{dp_0(t)}{dt} = -N\lambda p_0(t) + \mu p_1(t)$; $\dfrac{dp_N(t)}{dt} = \lambda p_{N-1}(t) - \mu p_N(t)$

$p_n(t) = \dbinom{N}{n}\dfrac{\lambda^n(1 - e^{-(\lambda + \mu)t})^n\,(\mu + \lambda\,e^{-(\lambda + \mu)t})^{N-n}}{(\lambda + \mu)^N}$.

6 $p_n = \dbinom{N}{n}\left(\dfrac{\lambda}{\lambda + \mu}\right)^n\left(\dfrac{\mu}{\lambda + \mu}\right)^{N-n}$.

7   Replication of each gene is a random process which proceeds at an average rate λ.

Distribution function is $p_N(\tau) = (1 - e^{-\lambda\tau})^N$.

Density function is $\lambda N\,e^{-\lambda\tau}(1 - e^{-\lambda\tau})^{N-1}$.

15 $\Pr(\text{No. served} = N) = \dfrac{e^{-\rho N}}{N!}(\rho N)^{N-1}$.

17 $T_2(s) = (\gamma + 1 - s)/\gamma$; $T_3(s) = [(\gamma + 1)(\gamma + 2) - (3\gamma + 2).s]/\gamma^2$

$T_4(s) = [(\gamma + 1)(\gamma + 2)(\gamma + 3) - (6\gamma^2 + 14\gamma + 6)\,s + 3\gamma s^2]/\gamma^3$.

18 $E\{M\} = 1 + \dfrac{(N - 1)}{\gamma} + \dfrac{(N - 1)(N - 2)}{\gamma^2} + \cdots + \dfrac{(N - 1)!}{\gamma^{N-1}}$.

Index